PIPE FITTINGS

NIPPLES

PIPE LENGTHS UP TO 22 FT.

STRAIGHT COUPLING

REDUCING COUPLING

COUPLING

NUT

CAP

STRAIGHT TEE

REDUCING TEE

STREET TEE

STRAIGHT CROSS

REDUCING CROSS

90° ELBOW

90° ELBOW

90° ELBOW

45° ELBOW

REDUCING ELBOW

90° STREET ELBOW

45° STREET ELBOW

45° Y-BEND

REDUCING TEE

REDUCER

UNION (3 PARTS)

PLUG

BUSHING

CAP

RETURN BEND

90°

45°

UNION ELBOWS

STREET

UNION TEES

PLUG

45° ELBOW

TEE

MEASURES OF CAPACITY

1 cup	=	8 fl oz
2 cups	=	1 pint
2 pints	=	1 quart
4 quarts	=	1 gallon
2 gallons	=	1 peck
4 pecks	=	1 bushel

STANDARD STEEL PIPE ((All Dimensions in inches)

Nominal Size	Outside Diameter	Inside Diameter	Nominal Size	Outside Diameter	Inside Diameter
⅛	0.405	0.269	1	1.315	1.049
¼	0.540	0.364	1¼	1.660	1.380
⅜	0.675	0.493	1½	1.900	1.610
½	0.840	0.622	2	2.375	2.067
¾	1.050	0.824	2½	2.875	2.469

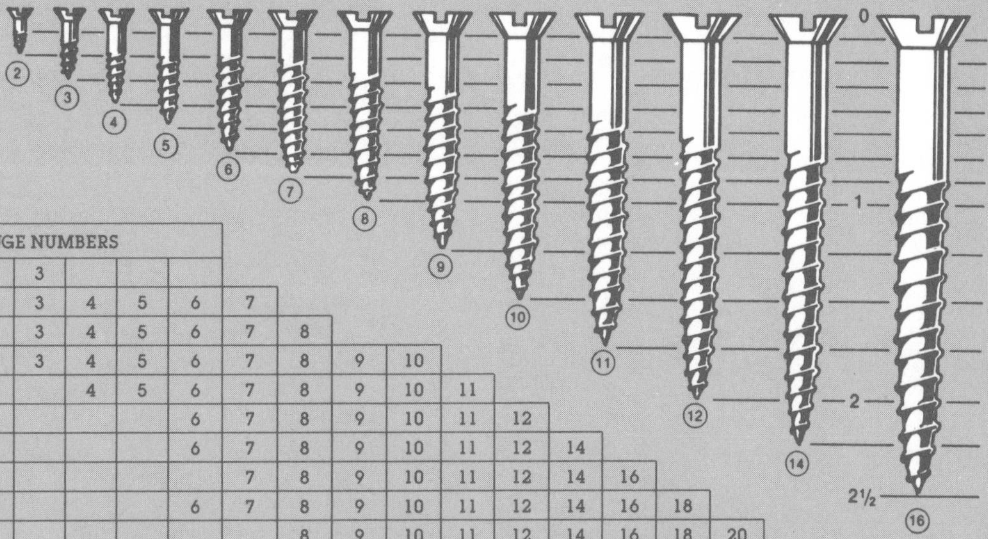

WOOD SCREWS

LENGTH	GAUGE NUMBERS																	
¼ INCH	0	1	2	3														
⅜ INCH			2	3	4	5	6	7										
½ INCH			2	3	4	5	6	7	8									
⅝ INCH				3	4	5	6	7	8	9	10							
¾ INCH					4	5	6	7	8	9	10	11						
⅞ INCH							6	7	8	9	10	11	12					
1 INCH							6	7	8	9	10	11	12	14				
1¼ INCH								7	8	9	10	11	12	14	16			
1½ INCH							6	7	8	9	10	11	12	14	16	18		
1¾ INCH									8	9	10	11	12	14	16	18	20	
2 INCH									8	9	10	11	12	14	16	18	20	
2¼ INCH										9	10	11	12	14	16	18	20	
2½ INCH													12	14	16	18	20	
2¾ INCH														14	16	18	20	
3 INCH															16	18	20	
3½ INCH																18	20	24
4 INCH																18	20	24

WHEN YOU BUY SCREWS, SPECIFY (1) LENGTH, (2) GAUGE NUMBER, (3) TYPE OF HEAD—FLAT, ROUND, OR OVAL (4) MATERIAL— STEEL, BRASS, BRONZE, ETC., (5) FINISH—BRIGHT, STEEL BLUED, CADMIUM, NICKEL, OR CHROMIUM PLATED

Popular Mechanics

do-it-yourself encyclopedia

The complete, illustrated home reference guide from the world's most authoritative source for today's how-to-do-it information.

Volume 19

PLUMBING

to

POWER TOOLS

HEARST DIRECT BOOKS

NEW YORK

Acknowledgements

The Popular Mechanics Encyclopedia is published with the consent and cooperation of POPULAR MECHANICS Magazine.

For POPULAR MECHANICS Magazine:

Editor-in-Chief: *Joe Oldham*
Managing Editor: *Bill Hartford*
Special Features Editor: *Sheldon M. Gallager*
Automotive Editor: *Wade A. Hoyt, SAE*
Home and Shop Editor: *Steve Willson*
Electronics Editor: *Stephen A. Booth*
Boating, Outdoors and Travel Editor: *Timothy H. Cole*
Science Editor: *Dennis Eskow*

Popular Mechanics Encyclopedia

Project Director: *Boyd Griffin*
Manufacturing: *Ron Schoenfeld*
Assistant Editors: *Cynthia W. Lockhart Peter McCann, Rosanna Petruccio*
Production Coordinator: *Peter McCann*

The staff of Popular Mechanics Encyclopedia is grateful to the following individuals and organizations:

Editor: *C. Edward Cavert*
Editor Emeritus: *Clifford B. Hicks*
Production: *Layla Productions*
Production Director: *Lori Stein*
Book Design: *The Bentwood Studio*
Art Director: *Jos. Trautwein*
Design Consultant: *Suzanne Bennett & Associates*
Illustrations: *AP Graphics, Evelyne Johnson Associates, Popular Mechanics Magazine, Vantage Art.*

Contributing Writers: Penelope Angell, *Pottery anyone can make*, page 2401; Walter E. Burton, *Portable saw pinch-hits as a cutoff machine*, page 2421; John Capostosto, *Pool table you can build*, page 2364; *Bumper-pool table in a small space*, page 2372; George Daniels, *Power tool tuneup*, page 2406; Bob Eckert, *Abrasive cutoff machine*, page 2419; Paul D. Fiebich, *Roll-away stand holds router and drill*, page 2417; Eben H. Gustafson, *Plywood cutoff jig you can build*, page 2362; Jackson Hand, *Stands for your power tools*, page 2412; Arnold H. Huehn, *Shrubbery light*, page 2400; Susan Lancaster, *Potter's wheel you can make*, page 2403; Jim McIntosh, *Working with plastic pipe*, page 2337; Richard V. Nunn, *Plumbing: and introduction*, page 2308; *Bathroom plumbing problems*, page 2324; Don Shiner, *Screened porch you can build*, page 2382; Robert W. Turek, *Mercury vapor lamp uses less energy*, page 2397; William G. Waggoner, *Retractable casters for your tool stands*, page 2416; Steven Willson, *Relocate a toilet*, page 2341; Craig Wilson, *Screened porch from your garage*, page 2387.

ISBN 0-87851-172-5

Library of Congress 85-81760

10 9 8 7 6 5 4

PRINTED IN THE UNITED STATES OF AMERICA

Contents

Plumbing: an introduction

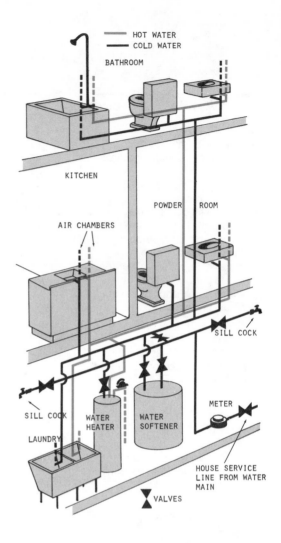

WATER DISTRIBUTION in a typical home comes through a water main and meter and then splits at the water heater. Under at least 60 pounds pressure per square inch, the water supply must be turned off before any repairs are made. Leaks at fittings and fixtures are the usual trouble spots.

■ HOME PLUMBING problems can be scary because the trouble is hidden in a tube and you can't see it. The fact is that only two basic problems can exist: the pipes and valves spring leaks; the pipes and drains become clogged. The solution to any plumbing problem is strictly mechanical and follows a fairly simple repair procedure, which is detailed below.

But before you tackle any plumbing problem, you should know how your home's supply and drainage systems work, and have a speaking acquaintance with their nomenclature.

The fresh water that comes into your home is supplied by either a public utility or a deep well in your yard. It is under pressure. If furnished by a public utility, the pressure is usually about 60 pounds per square inch (psi). If supplied by a deep well system, the water is pumped at 40 to 80 psi. The waste that goes out of your home flows into a public sewer or a septic system in your yard. Drains are not normally under pressure; gravity empties them.

Since fresh water is under pressure, you must always—*without fail*—turn off the water at the valve where it enters the house—or at the fixture—before you make repairs. You do not have to turn off the water to make repairs to drains.

The parts of a plumbing system are the *pipes* (copper, galvanized steel, cast iron, and/or plastic), the *valves* (faucets), and the *fixtures* (toilets, sinks, lavatories, bathtubs). The connections for the pipes, valves, and fixtures are called *fittings*. Plumbing accessories go by regular names such as pipe hangers, strainers, aerators, clamps, etc.

In and out of the house

The water coming into your home is controlled by a main valve which may be located in your basement, a utility closet, or outside under the water meter. This main supply pipe splits at the water heater. One pipe continues on and branches off to supply the cold water to the sinks, lavatories, tubs, clothes washer, toilets. The hot water pipe, from the water heater, also branches off to the various fixtures that supply hot water; sinks, lavatories, tubs, and so forth.

While fresh water comes in below the house,

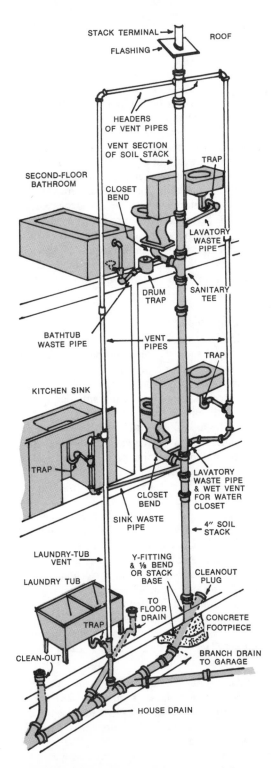

STACK TERMINAL → ROOF
FLASHING →

HEADERS OF VENT PIPES

VENT SECTION OF SOIL STACK

SECOND-FLOOR BATHROOM

CLOSET BEND

TRAP

LAVATORY WASTE PIPE

DRUM TRAP

SANITARY TEE

BATHTUB WASTE PIPE

VENT PIPES

KITCHEN SINK

TRAP

TRAP

LAVATORY WASTE PIPE & WET VENT FOR WATER CLOSET

CLOSET BEND

SINK WASTE PIPE

4" SOIL STACK

LAUNDRY-TUB VENT

Y-FITTING & 1/8 BEND OR STACK BASE

CLEANOUT PLUG

LAUNDRY TUB

TO FLOOR DRAIN

CONCRETE FOOTPIECE

TRAP

BRANCH DRAIN TO GARAGE

CLEAN-OUT

HOUSE DRAIN

THE WASTE SYSTEM in a typical home involves a soil stack to which all waste fixtures (lavatories, sinks, tubs, toilets) are connected. Clogging is the No. 1 problem; especially look for trouble in the fixture trap area or at the base of the soil stack near the cleanout plug.

drains start at the top of the house. The waste pipes slope from the fixtures and connect to a vertical pipe called the *main drain* pipe. Another vertical pipe called a *soil stack* runs vertically and parallel to the main drain. It is connected to the main drain and the top of it sticks out above the roof of the house and funnels away odors within the main drain. It also breaks a vacuum in the drain so the pipes connected to it from toilets, sinks, lavatories, etc., can flow freely. Main drains have a tee with a clean-out plug at the bottom of the drain pipe where it connects to the sewer. The clean-out plug is removed with a wrench.

Most drain pipes are *trapped,* ie., they have a sharp bend in them directly below the drain opening or several feet down the line. They are shaped like the letter "P" or "S." Another type trap, usually connected to a bathtub drain between the floor joists, is called a *drum trap* because it resembles a Civil War drum in shape. It is fairly small and has a clean-out plug.

The prime purpose of a trap is to form a kind of water "dam" between the fixture and the main drain. This dam prevents odors from the drain from working their way back through the drain pipe and out the opening in the sink, lavatory, toilet. Odors can't penetrate water barriers very well. Traps also snag valuables that may wash down the drain opening: rings, contact lenses, coins. And traps catch debris before it can go farther into the system and seriously clog the pipes. It is easier to clean a drain than a sewer pipe, although debris sometimes finds its way into the main system.

PIPE LEAKS can be stopped in an emergency with clamp devices which have a gasket that fits between the clamp and the leak in the pipe. The clamp is secured by bolts and nuts. Other leak stoppers include plastic electrician's tape for pinhole leaks and epoxy cement for leaks at fittings. All leak quick-fixes are temporary; replace the pipe or fitting just as soon as possible.

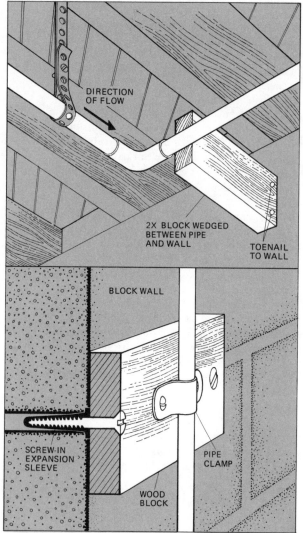

WATER PIPES sometimes are noisy because of water pressure and the sudden opening or closing of a faucet. You can stop the noise by blocking the pipes where they make 90° turns with a block of wood. Also make sure straight runs are held tightly with pipe hangers.

So, like electricity, the plumbing in your home makes a circuit: fresh water in; waste water out. It sounds simple enough; and it is.

All about pipes

Water pipes can leak, freeze, rattle and pound. They almost never clog because they are under pressure and there is nothing in a properly-filtered water supply to cause clogging. If the water supply dwindles to a trickle or stops completely, look for trouble with the pressure: too many valves open at one time, pipes too small to handle the water demand, or a low pumping pressure at the utility or your own water supply well. The low pressure problem also can stem (but not often) from a leak in a pipe or fitting, a malfunctioning valve, or a frozen pipe. In some areas, the pipes can *lime* shut from mineral deposits in the water. To determine whether this is the case, first turn off the water. Then disconnect a pipe at the fitting. Lime builds up around the inside walls of the pipe. It is a hard, whitish deposit. If this is the problem, call in a professional plumber. Do not try to force chemicals through the pipes to remove lime.

Leaking pipes

Pipes most often spring leaks at the fittings. Corrosion is the problem. Or you may discover a leak in the wall of a pipe along its run. Actually this, too, is a corrosion problem. There are a couple of techniques to handle this situation quickly.

1. If the pipe is leaking at a fitting, try tightening the pipe into the fitting gently. Use two pipe wrenches on galvanized steel pipe—one on the fitting and one on the pipe; the jaws of the wrenches should be facing in opposite directions. If the leak is in copper pipe, the fitting will have to be resoldered or replaced.

2. If the pipe is leaking along the run, you may be able to *temporarily* stop the flow of water with a clamp device, plastic electrician's tape, a self-tapping metal screw with a washer, and/or epoxy cement. All are available at most home centers and hardware stores. The clamp and gasket, which fits around the pipe in a clamshell configuration, usually is the most efficient. The metal screw/washer, tape, and epoxy sometimes work, but not always, depending on the size of the hole or crack in the pipe.

Caution: All leak-stoppers are for emergency use. Replace the pipe as soon as possible.

Noise in and from pipes is caused by water creating shock waves. What happens is that when a faucet is turned off—especially in a long horizontal pipe—a shock wave is created where the pipe changes its directional run. You hear a hammering or pounding noise caused by the shock vibrations. There are two ways to handle this; one technique is fairly easy and inexpensive; the other is more complicated and time-consum-

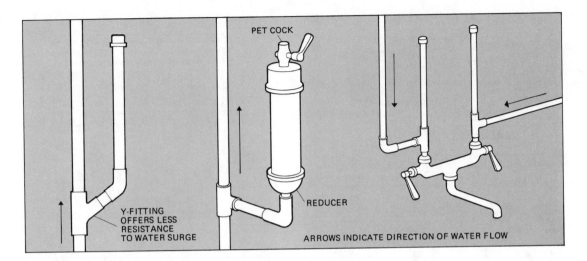

PET COCK

Y-FITTING
OFFERS LESS
RESISTANCE
TO WATER SURGE

REDUCER

ARROWS INDICATE DIRECTION OF WATER FLOW

AIR CHAMBERS which you can make, or buy at home centers, stop the hammering noise in pipes. The hammer is caused by trapped air in the system; the chambers "pad" this noise. If the system has air chambers and you still hear hammering, check the chambers for sediment and scale.

ing, but not difficult.

1. Try adding pipe clamps (strap hangers) at about 4 ft. intervals along the pipe run. The clamps may be attached to joists, studs, and other framing members. Or you may have to insert blocks of wood behind the pipe, at 6 ft. intervals, and fasten the blocks to the wall then fasten the pipe to the block with a clamp.

A variation is to block the pipe with a piece of scrap wood wedged between a wall or framing member and the pipe where the pipe makes a directional turn. The wedge block (2x4, 2x6) should not put any stress on the pipe; a snug fit is adequate.

2. Add a noise-reducing air chamber; it absorbs an overflow of water. The chamber, which can be just a length of pipe capped at one end, contains air which helps cushion the thrust of the water when a faucet is closed quickly. Or you can buy a reducer chamber to solve the problem. Most reducers have a pet cock or valve to release any vacuum in the reducer. With the pipe chamber, you have to turn off the water and unscrew the cap from time-to-time to break the vacuum.

Frozen pipes

Prevention is the best cure for frozen pipes. If freezing is a frequent problem, you may be able to solve it by wrapping the pipes with pipe insulation.

If insulation is impractical, a length of pipe heat tape is inexpensive and easy to install. Heat tape is basically a heating element embedded in a sleeve of insulation. You spiral the tape around the pipes and plug it into regular housepower when temperatures fall. You can buy heat tapes with thermostats. When the temperature drops to about 35°F., the thermostat automatically switches on the tape.

Freezing sill cocks may be your biggest problem. Sill cocks are the exterior faucet-like fittings to which you hook your garden hose. Just inside the wall, sill cock lines usually have shut-off valves. Thus you can close off that final leg in the system and drain it by opening the sill cock. If your plumbing system does not have this drainage feature, you can substitute a frost-free sill cock which has a compression valve 12 in. from the sill cock opening. The valve is inside the house.

Techniques for thawing frozen pipes depend on how accessible the pipes are. In any of the methods explained below, open the faucet nearest the frozen section of pipe before heat is applied to the pipe. The heat creates steam inside the pipe, which can break the fittings or damage the faucet.

If the pipe is horizontal in an open span, wrap the pipe with several layers of old toweling or burlap. Secure it with string. Then pour boiling water over the cloth until the ice in the pipe melts.

If the pipe is vertical in an open span, you can thaw it with a propane torch, if the flame from the torch is shielded so it doesn't scorch or set fire

MATERIAL DIFFERENCE

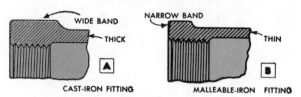

WIDE BAND

THICK

CAST-IRON FITTING

NARROW BAND

THIN

MALLEABLE-IRON FITTING

A

B

MALLEABLE FITTINGS

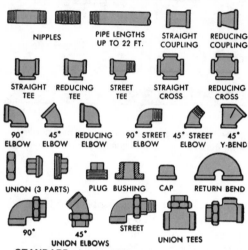

NIPPLES

PIPE LENGTHS UP TO 22 FT.

STRAIGHT COUPLING

REDUCING COUPLING

STRAIGHT TEE

REDUCING TEE

STREET TEE

STRAIGHT CROSS

REDUCING CROSS

90° ELBOW

45° ELBOW

REDUCING ELBOW

90° STREET ELBOW

45° STREET ELBOW

45° Y-BEND

UNION (3 PARTS)

PLUG

BUSHING

CAP

RETURN BEND

90°

45°

UNION ELBOWS

STREET

UNION TEES

STANDARD plumbing fittings include these shapes for most copper and plastic installations as well as galvanized steel. Malleable-iron fittings are thinner than cast-iron fittings, if this is a consideration. Copper and plastic fittings are approximately the same thickness.

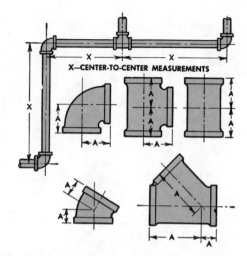

X—CENTER-TO-CENTER MEASUREMENTS

X

X

X

A

A

A

A

A

A

A

A

PIPE RUNS are measured from the center of the fittings. Or the run can be measured from the face of one fitting to the face of the adjoining fitting PLUS ½. or ⅝ in. at each fitting.

ALL PIPE—galvanized steel, copper, plastic—is measured by the inside diameter (ID) of the pipe. The fittings are sold by the ID measurement. Pipe goes into fittings ½-in. for copper and plastic and ⅝-in. for galvanized steel. Add this measurement when buying pipe.

to the materials near the pipe. This is dangerous under any circumstances; be very careful.

If the pipe is behind a wall, use a heat lamp to penetrate the wall covering and melt the ice. Melting will be slow because you must keep the lamp far enough away from the wall covering to prevent scorching. Heat lamps become very hot.

If a drain pipe is iced shut, pour hot water into the drain opening until the ice breaks free. Or you can remove the trap (where the ice block usually is located), and soak the trap in warm water.

Working with galvanized pipe

Most home center, hardware, and plumbing supply stores stock and sell pre-cut and threaded galvanized steel pipe in a wide range of sizes and lengths. You'll also find a variety of fittings for all sizes. If special lengths of pipe are needed, you can have them cut and threaded at a plumbing shop.

Pipe diameters are *always* measured from the inside—not outside—of the pipe wall. Length of run is from one end of the threads to the other

end of the threads—not where the threads stop on the smooth outer section of the pipe. Your measurement should be from the face of one fitting to the face of the opposite fitting PLUS 1¼ in. The extra length is for depth of threads in the fittings, which should be from about ½ to ⅝ in. Threads on galvanized steel pipe are slightly tapered. Therefore, when the threads are turned into a fitting, the threads have a "wedging" action that helps prevent leaks. Pipe sizes and fittings are standard. Example: if your plumbing system has ¾ in. galvanized steel pipe, any ¾-in. replacement pipe or fittings will match it. Steel and wrought iron pipe are sold in sizes from ⅛ in. to 6 in. in diameter.

Basic tools needed for galvanized steel pipe assembly include two 12 in. pipe wrenches, hacksaw, metal file, tape measure and a metal vise. Materials needed are pipe joint compound or plastic pipe tape, the pipe, and the necessary fit-

UNION FITTINGS are *always* needed when assembling galvanized steel pipe runs. The unions let you turn the pipe either direction in the standard fittings. This is necessary when replacing old pipe runs or assembling new pipe runs.

SEAL PIPE THREADS with either plastic threading tape or pipe joint compound, which has the consistency of putty. The tape should wrap around the threads in the direction the threads turn into the pipe fitting. Always put joint compound on the male threads of the pipe.

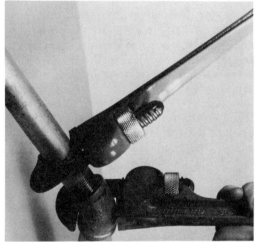

DOUBLE WRENCH galvanized pipe assembly and disassembly. The jaws of the pipe wrenches are opposed—opposite each other, as shown here. Keep one wrench on the fitting and the other on the pipe. To remove pipe in an existing run, use a hacksaw and cut the pipe at an angle—about 45°.

PLASTIC PIPE fittings have tiny shoulders inside the fittings against which the pipe butts tightly. If the pipe does not fit tightly against the shoulder, the connection probably will leak. Before buying and working with plastic pipe, make sure it conforms to your plumbing code.

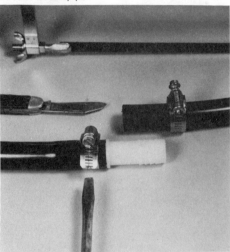

FLEXIBLE plastic pipe is assembled with straight or elbow connectors and clamps. The clamps slip over the pipe before the connectors are inserted. Clamps are similar to those used for radiator hoses in autos. They are turned tight with a screwdriver and/or wrench.

CUTTING plastic pipe may be done in two ways: with a hacksaw and miter box or with a tube cutter, which usually is recommended for copper pipe. Either way, the cut must be square and the burrs (cutting residue) on the pipe removed for a good, tight fit.

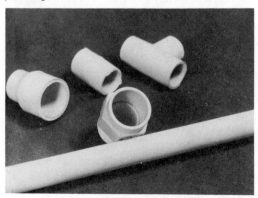

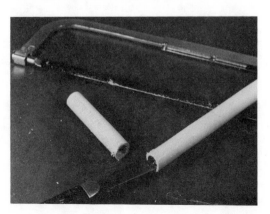

"DRY" ASSEMBLE the pipe run first—without the solvent. Put the pipe into the fittings tightly and set the pipe/fittings along the pipe run route. If the run does not fit, now is the time to cut and trim the pipe to fit the run perfectly.

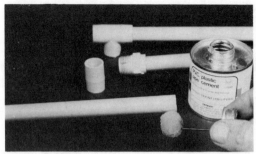

APPLY CEMENT to the pipe in a band about ½-in. wide. Use the type of cement recommended for the pipe. The cement should be spread fairly thin. Then slightly twist the pipe into the fitting so the cement forms a bead around the top of the fitting.

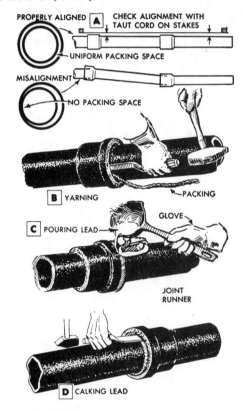

HUB-AND-SPIGOT drainage (sewer) pipe is assembled with oakum packing and molten lead. In vertical installations, the hub (thick end) faces "upstream". In horizontal installations, a joint runner is needed to fill the connection with lead. The hub also should face "upstream". Cast iron pipe is fractured by scoring it with a hacksaw and then breaking it at the scored line with a cold chisel and baby sledge hammer.

tings, i.e., tees, elbows, caps.

The one fitting that you *must* have is a union fitting. The union lets you turn the pipe being assembled in different directions.

Assembly procedures for steel pipe, illustrated in this article are extremely simple, but they take precise measurement and patience. Two pipe wrenches must be used to assemble (or disassemble) pipe runs: one wrench goes on the pipe fitting; the other wrench goes on the pipe. The jaws of the wrenches are opposite to provide better turning action.

Warning: pipe wrenches exert tremendous torque, so turn them gently. Too much pressure can crush the steel pipe. The jaws of the wrench are "loose" to conform with the diameter of the pipe. As the leverage is applied to the wrench handle, the jaws grip and hold the pipe tightly.

Pipe threads—*not* the threads inside the fittings—should be coated with pipe joint compound or covered with plastic tape to help deter leaks. Tape is less messy than joint compound, but it can be difficult to wrap. If you use tape, wrap it around the threads in the direction the threads will be turned into the fitting—usually clockwise.

Steel pipe in hot water runs should be kept as short as possible so the water will not lose heat in the run. Also steel pipe should not be used underground or under concrete walkways, driveways, patios, and so forth. Steel pipe should not be joined with copper pipe without an adaptor. The different metals set up a corrosive action.

Working with plastic pipe

Local plumbing codes permitting, plastic pipe is a do-it-yourselfer's dream. It is lightweight, fairly inexpensive, and goes together in a flash with just plastic pipe cement.

Plastic pipe is manufactured from ABS (acrylonitrile butadiene styrene), PVC (polyvinyl chloride), and CPVC (chlorinated polyvinyl chloride). PVC and ABS are used mostly for drain, waste and vent systems and as an underground electrical conduit. You can use CPVC for hot and cold water systems under pressure; the pipe is pressure-marked as to pounds per square inch (psi).

Plastic pipe is available in a range of sizes and lengths, although the standard length is 10 ft., and the diameter sizes most popular are ½ and ¾ in. Standard fittings include elbows, tees, adaptors for steel and copper pipe, caps, valves and straight couplings. The parts are "welded" together with a brushed-on solvent.

Two cautions: Make sure that plastic pipe is accepted by the building codes in your community; do not mix two types of plastic (ABS with CPVC for example) in the same installation.

Tools for working with plastic pipe are simple: a hacksaw and/or tube cutter, miter box, tape measure, small file, sandpaper, pocketknife and clean wiping cloth. Materials include the pipe, fittings and cement recommended for the type of plastic being used. If flexible plastic pipe is used, clamps will be needed to secure the pipe to the fittings.

Procedures for installing almost any plastic plumbing run include these:

1. Carefully measure the run. Add 1 in. of pipe length between each fitting; the extra pipe allows for the distance it goes into fittings.

2. Make a drawing of the plumbing project on graph paper showing the direction changes of the pipe and the number and type of fittings needed. Double check all measurements.

3. Cut the pipe to fit the run, using a hacksaw and miter box or tube cutter. Clean away any cutting debris on the pipe.

4. Dry assemble the pipe and fittings and match the assembled pipe to the plumbing run. Make any necessary adjustments.

5. Cement the pipe run, starting at one end of the run. Do not cement the entire project. Working piece-by-piece allows any adjustment if you have made a measuring mistake. Once cemented, the pipe has to be cut to be removed. It can not be pulled apart at the fittings like copper or galvanized steel pipe.

Drainage pipe

Working with drainage pipe looks frightening. It's large and heavy, and appears complicated. Actually, drainage pipe is easy to assemble—especially "no-hub" pipe which is connected with gaskets and clamps. Old-fashioned hub-and-spigot pipe is more difficult to handle because the pipe sections have to be filled with oakum and molten lead. This requires a heater for the lead and a "joint runner" to funnel the lead into the joint when the pipe is along a horizontal run.

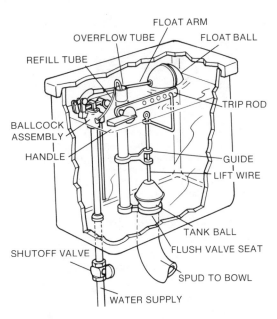

PARTS LOCATER for a typical flush tank. The tank may sit right on the back of the toilet bowl, or be connected to the bowl via a spud (shown).

You can cut cast iron pipe with a hacksaw. Or you can rent a roller cutter for small diameter pipe or a chain cutter for large diameter pipe. With a hacksaw, score the pipe about ⅛-in. deep around its circumference at the cut-off point. Then, at the scored line, tap the pipe with a baby sledge hammer to fracture it. The edges may be left rough since they will fit into a spigot or gasket. However, if the edges are really rough, smooth them with a cold chisel. Properly scored, the fracture will be smooth.

If hub-and-spigot pipe is used, the joint (hub) in a vertical run should face upward. The joint is first packed with oakum and then filled with molten lead. If the joint is on a horizontal run, it also is packed with oakum and filled with molten lead that is placed with a joint runner that you can rent.

If no-hub pipe is used, a no-hub gasket serves as a connector. In assembly, the pipe is cut and butted together. A clamp and sleeve is slipped onto the pipes after you are satisfied that the pipe joint is a fairly tight fit. The sleeve is centered on the joint and the clamps are tightened with a screwdriver or T-wrench. Elbow and tee fittings are assembled the same way.

TWO REPLACEABLE washers are in the ballcock valve: one in a groove (O-ring) around the stem and the other at the bottom of the stem. You can remove the washers with the tip of a screwdriver and press the new ones back in position.

WORN WASHERS in the ballcock assembly can cause a noisy toilet. In this type ballcock, remove the thumbscrews that hold the float arm assembly. Then remove the lifting arm. If the ballcock is the plastic type remove the valve cover. You will see an O-ring. Replace it.

Solving flush tank troubles

A flush tank is a water reservoir for the toilet. The tank contains an assembly of valves and floats that regulate the flow of water into the toilet bowl. The water in the tank is perfectly clean; don't be concerned about putting your hands into it for minor flush tank adjustments.

The best way to solve a flush tank problem is to isolate the problem. Below is a list of typical flush tank malfunctions and what you can do about them.

Inadequate flush. There's not enough water in the tank to complete the flush in the toilet bowl. Small ballcock assemblies have a screw on top of the ballcock at the float rod joint. Turn this screw up or down to lower the float arm and float ball. By lifting the float, you add water to the tank; by lowering the float, you lower the water. If the ballcock is the low profile type or has the float on the ballcock assembly, a knurled screw on top of the ballcock regulates the water, or a spring clip on the float is adjusted to raise or lower it. The water level should be about ¾ in. below the top of the overflow tube.

If the ballcock does not have an adjustment, try bending the float rod down for high water or up for low water. Bend the rod gently. Then flush the toilet to test the water level. You may have to bend or unbend the rod to get the water level needed.

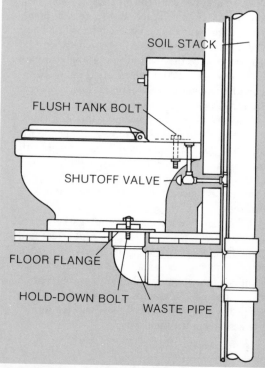

SOIL STACK

FLUSH TANK BOLT

SHUTOFF VALVE

FLOOR FLANGE

HOLD-DOWN BOLT

WASTE PIPE

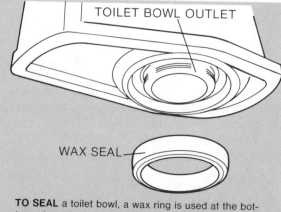

TOILET BOWL OUTLET

WAX SEAL

TO SEAL a toilet bowl, a wax ring is used at the bottom where the bowl slip-fits into the waste pipe. Do not assemble the bowl without the wax ring or the toilet will leak. It's a good idea to replace the hold-down bolts and caps (if any) when you change a bowl or even repair the seal.

CRITICAL MEASUREMENT for new toilet bowl is from the wall to the center of the waste pipe. Determine this by measuring from the wall to the center of the hold-down bolt. Or remove the toilet bowl and measure from the center of the pipe to the wall.

Constantly low water in the tank. The float ball may contain water which won't let it rise high enough to supply the necessary water supply. You can remove the float ball by unscrewing it counterclockwise from the rod. Or the tank ball, at the bottom of the tank, may be leaking so slowly that you can't hear the water. See "running water" category.

Splashing sounds. Chances are the refill tube is not discharging directly into the overflow. This water is used to form a seal in the toilet's trap to prevent odors from escaping from the main drain. Simply flush the toilet to check the water flow and reposition the tube into the overflow to solve the splashing problem. Splashing also may be caused by a worn inlet valve atop the ballcock assembly. Flush the toilet and look for leaks at this point while the tank is refilling. If the valve (actually its washer) is the problem, turn off the water and remove the valve. It is screwed to the ballcock housing. Inside, you will see a flat or O-ring washer. Replace this part and reassemble the unit. Then flush the toilet. If the problem still exists, replace the entire ballcock assembly. The cost is not prohibitive.

Tank is hard to flush. Look first at the lift wire guide attached to the overflow tube. Is the guide in alignment with the lift wire on the tank ball? If not, the lift wire can bind in the guide, causing a hard flush. The problem also can cause a running toilet because the tank ball doesn't seat properly in the flush valve seat.

Check also the flush handle and its linkage with the tank ball lift wire. There may be too much slack in the linkage. You can correct this by shortening the chain on the end of the trip lever, or repositioning the wire linkage in the holes in the trip lever. Look for corrosion at the base of the handle on the inside of the tank. Remove this with steel wool and tighten the nut that fastens the handle to the tank.

Singing flush tank. The sound can be caused by a faulty gasket in the ballcock assembly, or restricted water flow to the ballcock assembly. Washer replacement is detailed above. If the problem is restricted water flow, try opening the fixture valve completely. If not, look for corrosion at the valve or at the water opening to the ballcock unit. Both the valve and the ballcock may have to be changed.

Moisture on or around toilet. Condensation usually can be blamed. If the flush tank "sweats" during the summer months, try installing a foam liner or tank cover to stop this. Leaks at the bottom of the flush tank most likely are caused by

loose locknuts at the bottom of the ballcock assembly where the water supply connects. Try tightening this connection. Go easy; too much heft can crack the tank. If tightening doesn't stop the leak, turn off the water and replace the washers and gaskets at the bottom of the ballcock assembly.

Leaks around the base of the toilet bowl could be condensation, but, unfortunately, the trouble probably is a leak at the wax ring gasket between the bottom of the toilet and the sewer pipe. First try tightening the hold down bolts at the base of the toilet. If this doesn't work, you will have to replace the wax ring, which is detailed below. Don't delay this repair: the water leak can cause lots of damage to the structural members of the house.

A cracked flush tank or toilet bowl sometimes is the source of leaks and moisture. Here, the tank and/or the bowl must be replaced immediately. You cannot satisfactorily repair the cracks.

Unstopping a clogged toilet is not a pleasant project, but the following procedures can save you some time and trouble.

Do not flush the toilet, even though some of the water has drained from the bowl. Instead, bail out the excess water in the bowl so the water height is slightly below its normal level. The best way to bail is to wrap your hand and arm in several plastic garbage bags. Tie the tops of the bags loosely around the top of your forearm. The bags protect your hands and arms from the toilet mess.

Position a plumber's friend suction cup made especially for toilets in the bottom of the bowl. Work the plunger *extremely* hard and fast up and down in the bowl. Use all the muscle you can; 50 strokes is minimum. A pattycake action won't work. You should feel and hear the blockage break loose as the plunger travels up and down.

If the plunger doesn't work—after you've given it a fair try—use a closet auger to remove the blockage. This tool is threaded down through the bottom opening of the bowl and up and over a trap configuration and out the sewer pipe connection. You can either snag the blockage (usually a wash cloth or toy) and pull it out or force the blockage (paper and waste) down into the sewer pipe. Do not force an insoluble object into the main sewer. It will block the system.

Reseating or replacing a toilet bowl is easier than it might sound, although it requires patience.

First, make sure that it isn't against local codes for you to do the job. Some communities require

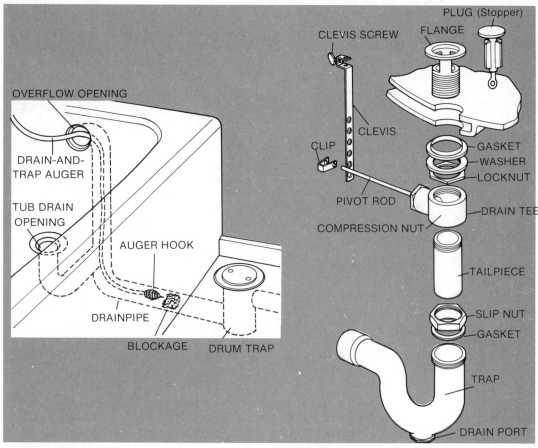

Labels in illustration: OVERFLOW OPENING, DRAIN-AND-TRAP AUGER, TUB DRAIN OPENING, AUGER HOOK, DRAINPIPE, BLOCKAGE, DRUM TRAP, CLEVIS SCREW, FLANGE, PLUG (Stopper), CLIP, CLEVIS, PIVOT ROD, COMPRESSION NUT, GASKET, WASHER, LOCKNUT, DRAIN TEE, TAILPIECE, SLIP NUT, GASKET, TRAP, DRAIN PORT

BATHTUB DRAINS sometimes respond to auger cleanout rather than suction. But try suction first. The auger can be inserted through the tub drain opening or down the overflow. Or, the trap may be opened (in older homes) and the auger worked back (or forward) from the trap.

ANATOMY of a sink/lavatory trap: The flange is set with plumber's putty. The trap is connected with slip nuts and O-ring gaskets. By unscrewing the compression nut, the pivot rod can be released from the bottom of the plug so the stopper can be removed.

a licensed plumber to make repairs/replacements.

Replacement and reseating is essentially the same. In replacement, you need to know the measurement from the wall in back of the toilet to the center of the toilet drain pipe. This is easy if the old bowl has been removed. If not, find the measurement from the wall to either of the toilet bowl hold-down bolts. If only one bolt (each side) holds the bowl, measure from the wall to the center of this bolt. The plumbing supply retailer can determine what size replacement unit is needed from these measurements.

To remove the old toilet bowl, pry or lift off the caps that hide the bowl bolts. Then turn out the bolts counterclockwise. Of course this should be done only after the water has been turned off and the flush tank and bowl have been emptied.

If the bolts won't budge, slide a hacksaw blade between the bottom of the bowl rim and the top of the floor and saw the bolts loose. Or if you in-

tend to replace the bowl, simply break the bowl into small pieces with a baby sledge hammer. Wear safety glasses during this operation; gloves are a good idea, too.

Once the bolts are free, you can lift the bowl straight off the floor flange and what's left of the wax ring seal. Carefully examine the area around the opening for wood decay. Rotted framing or flooring must be replaced before the bowl is reseated. The floor flange is fastened to the framing/flooring. Check it to see if it is in sound condition. If not, replace it; the cost is minimal.

A wax ring or wax sealer is used to waterproof the connection between the bottom of the bowl and the pipe. Turn the bowl upside down and fit the wax ring on the bowl projection. Or, if the floor flange is recessed slightly below the floor, install a wax ring with a plastic sleeve on the bowl. The sleeve faces toward the pipe since it sets into the pipe. With a putty knife, spread toilet-bowl setting compound around the edge of the bowl rim. Thickness should be about ⅛- to ¼-in.

Lift the bowl, turn it over, and set it down over the pipe and onto the floor. Twist the bowl slightly so both the wax ring and compound "seats" properly. At this point, set a carpenter's level across the bowl and level the bowl by pushing it gently downward into the wax ring. If level can't be accomplished by pressing, you will have to shim under the bottom rim of the bowl with cedar shingle wedges. Keep the edges of the wedges under the rim so they don't show. A bead of tub caulking around the rim at the floor will hide any gaps.

Once in place, secure the bowl to the floor with hold-down bolts. Tighten the bolts carefully; too much pressure on the wrench can crack the bowl. Install the flush tank on the back of the bowl to complete the job.

Toilet seat replacement is simply an unbolt-the-old and bolt-down-the-new project. The locknuts fastening the seat to the bowl are directly under the hinged lids. Toilet seats are standard; one size usually fits all. Be careful tightening the new locknuts; too much pressure can crack the bowl.

Opening clogged drains

Like most plumbing problems, opening a clogged sink or tub drain involves a procedure:

first try one technique, then move to another if the first one fails.

If water in the bowl is slow draining but not completely clogged, try a chemical drain cleaner, following the manufacturer's instructions.

If the drain is completely blocked, a plumber's friend (suction cup) may open it. Bail out most of the water in the bowl, leaving about ¾-in. If the bowl has an overflow, stuff a wet cloth into the overflow opening. Wedge it tight. Remove the strainer or stopper from the drain opening. Place the suction cup of the plumber's friend over the drain opening and seat the rim of it against the bottom of the bowl. Now bend over the handle of the plumber's friend and, without lifting the suction cup off the surface of the bowl, work the handle in an up-and-down action just as hard and fast as you possibly can. Use plenty of heft with the weight of your shoulders over the handle. Give the handle at least 50 downward strokes. Don't give up.

During the plunging process, you probably will hear and/or see the drain open and the water run out. When the drain is clear, flush fresh water through the pipe and add chemical drain cleaner following manufacturer's directions.

If, after an honest try, the drain will not open, place a bucket under the trap of the bowl and

ANATOMY of a faucet: Designs may vary, but the working parts are similar. If the faucet is leaking at the top, the washer or packing probably is the cause. If the faucet is leaking out the spout (body), the stem washer may be the problem.

O-RING WASHERS are used along the stem of some late model faucets. The washers snap into a channel or groove machined into the stem; they may be removed with the tip of a screwdriver or nail. If the faucet is leaking around top, this washer may be the cause.

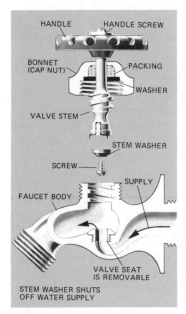

HANDLE   HANDLE SCREW

BONNET (CAP NUT)   PACKING

WASHER

VALVE STEM

STEM WASHER

SCREW

SUPPLY

FAUCET BODY

VALVE SEAT IS REMOVABLE

STEM WASHER SHUTS OFF WATER SUPPLY

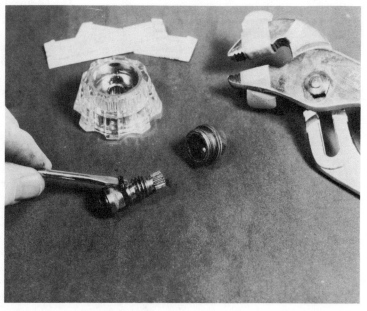

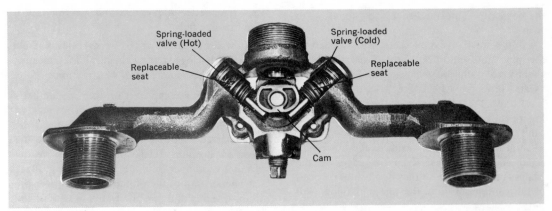

SINGLE-LEVER FAUCETS that are cam operated have spring-loaded valves and replaceable seats. The seats are removed with a screwdriver after the valves are removed—also with a screwdriver and/or wrench. If this type faucet is leaking, it's possible that dirt is lodged on the seat.

with a wrench remove the large nuts that hold the trap pipe to the tailpiece of the drain and the drain extension pipe. The water from the bowl will go into the bucket along with the clog which usually is stuck in the trap.

The clog may be beyond the trap. In this case, thread a plumber's snake or flexible auger into the drain extension and rod out the pipe. If the drain is still plugged after you reassemble the parts, the trouble is in the main drain, and it will have to be cleaned out at the clean-out plug. You can tell whether this main is stopped because the other drains in the household also will fail to flow properly—including the toilets.

Clogged bathtub drains often can be opened by using the same technique as for sink and lavatory drains. However, if the plunger treatment won't work after you have given it a fair chance, remove the escutcheon plate that covers the overflow and, usually, the trip lever that operates the tub's stopper.

Thread a flexible auger down the overflow pipe so it inches into the main drain pipe. Then twist the auger until you feel the clog break. Flush the system with fresh water and add chemical drain cleaner.

Bathtubs in older homes have a drum trap which usually is located near the tub between joists under the flooring. There is an access opening in the floor to get at this trap. It could be in the bathroom next to the tub, or in a closet that fronts or backs the tub. The cover over the trap may be fastened by screws, or you may have to just pry the cover up and off with the tip of a screwdriver. On top of the trap is a lug which can be turned with an adjustable wrench. Remove the top and clean out the trap. If the debris is not

in the trap, you can run the auger through the pipes that connect to the drum trap and open the drain.

When faucets leak

Leaky faucets not only waste water and the energy to heat water, but get on your nerves with a steady dripping sound. Repairing leaky faucets, and those with other problems such as rattles and excessive moisture, is an easy job that shouldn't take over 30 minutes to complete if you follow these procedures for repair.

First, turn off the water at the shut-off valve below the fixture or at the main water valve.

There are two basic types of faucets: compression and cartridge. Some of the cartridge faucets are claimed by their manufacturer to be "washerless," but they still utilize O-rings and gaskets which can wear out, causing leaks and other problems.

Compression faucets are the single handle or lever type that have a packing nut, packing, and a threaded stem with a washer on the end of it. The washer compresses against a valve seat in the faucet housing and shuts off the water. Hence: compression faucet. What goes bad here is the packing or washer. This is normal, caused by wear.

To repair a compression faucet, regardless of its design, first remove the handle. It is held by a screw which may be located under a decorative escutcheon cap. The cap can be pried up and off the handle with a tip of a screwdriver. Or the handle screw may be a set-screw located in back of the handle. You will need an Allen wrench to loosen the screw. Pull the handle straight up and off the stem. Use a little force, if necessary, from

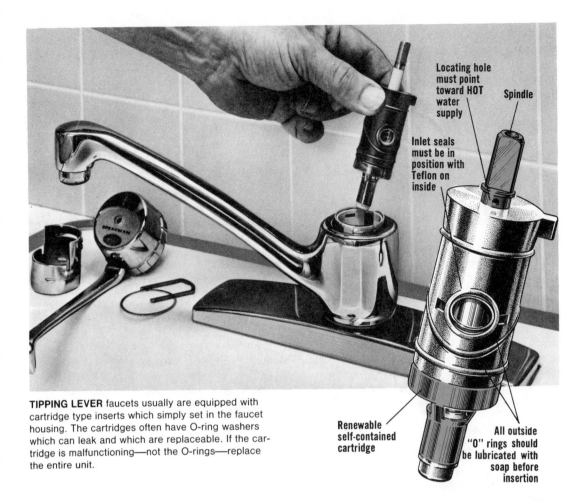

Locating hole must point toward HOT water supply

Spindle

Inlet seals must be in position with Teflon on inside

TIPPING LEVER faucets usually are equipped with cartridge type inserts which simply set in the faucet housing. The cartridges often have O-ring washers which can leak and which are replaceable. If the cartridge is malfunctioning—not the O-rings—replace the entire unit.

Renewable self-contained cartridge

All outside "O" rings should be lubricated with soap before insertion

a screwdriver. Remove the packing nut, which unscrews counterclockwise. An adjustable wrench does the best job without marring the chrome finish. Then, with the handle back on the stem (but not fastened with the screw), turn out the stem. At the top of the stem you will see either a washer or packing string; at the bottom of the stem you will see a washer held by a screw.

If the faucet is leaking around the cap, replace the packing washer or gasket or string. If the unit is leaking out the spout, change the stem washer. It is recommended that you use new replacement parts, which are very inexpensive. Don't try to make-do. When you change one part, change the other at the same time. Also, while the stem is accessible, polish it with steel wool to remove any corrosion. Pay special attention to the stem washer. If it looks ragged and chewed, instead of worn smooth, chances are the valve seat against which the washer compresses is rough and pitted. You can smooth this seat with a seat dressing tool on sale at most home center and hardware stores.

Or you may be able to replace the valve seat, which screws into the faucet housing. A hex-type wrench is used for this; it also is sold at home centers and hardwares.

To complete the job, reassemble the faucet in reverse order and turn on the water.

Cartridge faucets have four basic designs: tipping lever or valve; ball; disc; cartridge. Replacement parts usually are sold in kits for the specific brand of faucet. Sometimes you can find individual parts, but the kits are the best buy. Know what type of faucet you have before you shop for parts. Delta faucet parts, for example, will not fit Peerless faucets.

Single lever faucets (tipping lever type) have spring-loaded valves for both hot and cold water. The valves are located in a V configuration next to the spout. To remove the escutcheon housing, unscrew the spout of the faucet and lift both off. A cap covers each valve and it may be removed with a screwdriver or adjustable wrench. Problems with this faucet are worn valve stems and

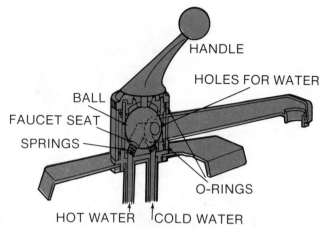

HANDLE

HOLES FOR WATER

BALL

FAUCET SEAT

SPRINGS

O-RINGS

HOT WATER   COLD WATER

DISASSEMBLED ball faucet is shown above left. The springs are under the washers (O-rings) at the bottom of the faucet. You pry out the washers with the tip of a screwdriver and press them back into place with your fingers. The large end of the washer should be in an "up" position. Washer and spring kits are available; take along the old parts for a match. Above right, ball faucets are also the tipping type. The handle (lever) is removed by releasing a set screw at the base. Unscrew the faucet cap to get at the ball and seat assembly. The parts simply lift out of the housing. If the faucet is leaking at the cap, try tightening the cap. If this doesn't work, replace the gasket or O-ring at the cap.

seats. Both parts may be replaced; they are removed from the faucet housing with a faucet seating wrench which you can buy for this purpose. The procedure is extremely simple: just remove the old stems and seats and replace them with similar new ones. If the spout is leaking where it joins the handle assembly, replace the O-ring washer.

DISC FAUCETS are self-contained. However, they do have three seals at the bottom of the cartridge which can work loose. Remove the handle assembly, escutcheon, and cartridge screws. Then lift out the cartridge. Push the seals into place; reassemble the faucet.

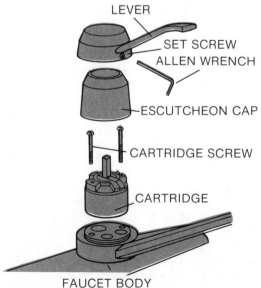

LEVER

SET SCREW

ALLEN WRENCH

ESCUTCHEON CAP

CARTRIDGE SCREW

CARTRIDGE

FAUCET BODY

Ball cartridge faucets have a single lever handle that tips up and down to open/close the faucet and moves sideways to supply hot/cold water. The faucet handle is held to the ball assembly by a setscrew usually found on the handle at the front of the faucet. Loosen this screw, remove the handle, and then unscrew the knurled cap counterclockwise to get at the ball parts. Under the cap you will find a cap and cam assembly, an O-ring washer to seal it, and the ball. Lift out the ball and look down at the housing. There are two or three faucet seats that are topped by O-ring washers pinched into the housing and springs under the washers.

You can remove the O-ring washers with the tip of a screwdriver (be careful) and then flip out the springs. Just install the new springs and reseat the O-ring washers. Then replace the ball, cam, cap and O-ring washer. Reassemble the handle parts.

A disc faucet has three cartridge seals at the bottom of the cartridge; these can become worn and cause the faucet to leak or drip.

A setscrew holds on the handle; loosen it with an Allen or hex wrench. Lift off the handle and the escutcheon cap underneath the handle. The cartridge is held by two or three screws. Remove these and lift up the cartridge. You will see the O-ring seals at the bottom of the cartridge. Remove and replace these; a screwdriver is the best tool.

If the seals are not causing the problem, it is recommended that you buy a new disc cartridge replacement; don't try to repair the old one.

Cartridge sleeve faucets usually are single-lever, and the lever or handle is turned to the hot or cold water selection and then tipped up to turn on the water. To get at the cartridge, the lever is pushed down past the "off" position and the escutcheon is pried off with a screwdriver after the lever screw at the top of the escutcheon is removed. This screw may be hidden by a decorative escutcheon plate which is a friction fit on top of the lever housing.

Once off, you will see a retaining nut. Remove it with a screwdriver, adjustable wrench, or pliers. Lift out the grooved sleeve directly below the retaining nut. At the top of the cartridge you will see a tiny clip that holds the cartridge in the faucet housing. Pull this clip straight out with pliers or the tip of a screwdriver. The cartridge now may be removed by pulling it straight up with pliers. If the cartridge has O-ring washers, replace these, which may be the cause of the leak. Or replace the entire cartridge and then reassemble the faucet. As a rule, it is best to replace the cartridge instead of trying to repair it. The cost is minimal.

Bathtub faucets operate almost the same way as sink and lavatory faucets except they are horizontal instead of vertical. If the tub faucet is a cartridge type, it may have several retaining clips that have to be pulled before the cartridge can be released from the housing. Also, the cartridge may be color coded so you can insert it properly into its housing. This will be noted on the replacement cartridge package (usually) or you can match the cartridge configuration of the old part with the new for the proper assembly.

Other plumbing connections

Shower heads, kitchen sink spray hoses, and washing machine connections fall into this category, and you'll find these parts easy to replace. Since new parts are not costly, it is recommended that you work with new parts instead of trying to repair the old ones. You will save time and effort.

Shower heads are connected to a riser type pipe that works off the bathtub faucet. The shower head is simply screwed onto this pipe; an adjustable wrench is used to remove or install it.

Troubles with shower heads usually are lime build-ups in the nozzle of the unit. By removing the shower head from its pipe, you may be able to disassemble the unit by removing the faceplate. It will turn counterclockwise. Once inside the head, you can clean the water holes in the face plate and the lime deposits in the water channels. Try soaking the head overnight in white vinegar,

which will loosen and remove the minerals.

Kitchen sink spray hoses usually go bad at the nozzle. Unfortunately, most spray nozzles are permanently attached to the hose, so the entire hose unit must be replaced if it doesn't work. But before you buy a new hose, try removing the nozzle. If it can be removed, you turn a coupling nut between the hose and the nozzle which exposes a snap ring and washer assembly. Remove these parts and the spray nozzle will disconnect from the hose.

If the unit must be replaced, it is coupled to the kitchen sink faucet directly under the spout of the faucet under the kitchen sink. You may need a basin wrench to turn the hex nut that attaches the hose to the faucet. Be sure to turn off the water before removing the hose. Also, insert the new hose through the hole in the sink before you connect the hose to the faucet fitting.

Washing machine connections are flexible hoses (similar to a garden hose) which connect to faucets with threaded spouts (similar to an exterior sill cock). The hoses usually have small screens at both the faucet and machine connections. If the washer won't fill with water, or the washer is slow-filling, check these screens to make sure they are not clogged with sediment from the water system. Often they are.

Water heater maintenance

The water heater probably is the most neglected appliance in any home. It goes right along heating water and you don't know it even exists—until the hot-water faucet flows cold. Water heaters actually take little maintenance, but there are a couple of checks you should make on a regular schedule.

Every month or so, press down on the relief valve of the heater, which is located on top of the unit. Let a little water trickle out so you know the valve is functioning properly. Also, open the heater drain every two months or so and let a couple of gallons of water flow out. This will remove any sediment from the bottom of the tank. If the tank is old, don't drain it. Draining could cause leaks.

If the water won't heat and the heater is electric powered, check the fuse box or circuit breaker at the main power entrance. If the heater runs on gas, the pilot light may be out. Instructions for lighting the pilot are embossed on the front of the heater near the pilot light panel. If, after checking these points, the heater still won't function, the problem probably is a malfunctioning element or thermocouple. Call a pro to fix this.

Bathroom plumbing problems you can fix

■ NOT ONLY CAN A LEAKY, dripping faucet become hazardous to your nervous system, it can cost you money—especially if the problem is on the hot-water side. Both the water and the energy used to heat it can go down the pipes at the rate of 5–7 gallons per day at just one tiny drop at a time.

The source of trouble generally is a worn faucet washer which is fastened to the bottom of the faucet stem. The first repair step is to turn off the water at the supply valve below the sink or lavatory, or at the main valve where water is piped into your home from the utility or a well. After closing either valve, open the problem faucet to make sure the water supply is off.

With a screwdriver, remove the faucet handle. The screw holding the handle may be under a decorative escutcheon which can be pried up and out of its seat with the tip of a screwdriver.

Unscrew the faucet cap that holds the stem in the faucet housing. Use a pipe wrench padded with soft cloth or smooth-jawed channel pliers to turn the cap counterclockwise. Slip the faucet handle back on the top of the stem and turn out the stem counterclockwise. The stem is threaded. Once out of the housing, remove the handle from the stem.

The washer is at the bottom of the stem on compression type faucets. It is held with a brass screw. Remove the screw and pry out the washer. Fit the new washer into the seat and secure it with the screw. You may have to buff the edges of the washer with sandpaper so the washer fits tightly into or onto the metal seat. Some faucets have O-ring washers along the stem. Most have flat washers below the cap. Some have string packing. Replace these washers or packing along with the seat washer. The string packing is simply wrapped around the stem.

If worn washers are a constant problem, the faucet's valve seat may be pitted. To repair this, turn off the water and remove the faucet stem. Then insert and connect a faucet seat grinder—an inexpensive tool available at hardware stores—into the faucet housing. Screw the adjustable nut on the grinding tool down enough so the faucet's cap nut catches a couple of threads after it's placed over the adjustable nut on the threaded grinding tool shaft. Now turn the grinding tool clockwise by its cross handle. Tighten the cap nut as you turn. Make two complete revolutions with the grinder. Then remove the cap nut and grinder, replace the washers, and reassemble the faucet.

Cartridge-type faucets also drip

"Never drip" cartridge faucets do drip sometimes, and the repair is similar to repairing compression faucets except that the entire cartridge may have to be replaced if the washers in it can't be switched. You can buy special repair kits for these faucets; take the old parts to the store for a perfect match.

To repair a tipping valve cartridge faucet, turn off the water at the supply or main valve. Remove the handle with a screwdriver and the cap with a pipe wrench or channel pliers. Be careful not to damage the shiny finish.

A tipping valve faucet has a ball-shaped fitting under the metal cap. Under the plastic cap over the ball is a washer. Replace this washer. In the curved plastic socket in which the ball fits, you will see several more (usually three) O-ring washers inserted in the plastic. Pry out these washers with the tip of a screwdriver and replace them with new washers inserted with your fingers.

If the cartridge is a tube, remove the escutcheon and a stop tube behind the handle. These faucets usually have a retaining clip or two that hold the cartridge in its housing. Pull these clips

;HER FITS into a metal "sleeve" at nd of the valve stem. Install the washer with a brass screw usually ded in the washer package.

VALVE SEAT GRINDER fits into faucet housing. The cap goes over the threaded shank (slip out cross handle) and is screwed to the housing.

O-RING WASHER above ball is the one that usually leaks. Three more O-ring washers are located at the bottom of the socket in which the ball fits.

straight up and out with pliers. Then replace the entire cartridge with a new one.

The cartridge may be coded via a flat side. Make sure this side is facing the sink or lavatory as it is inserted into the housing. If the repair is to a tub or shower, the flat or coded side should always face up.

On some faucets, the spout has to be removed to get at the cartridge. First, remove the retaining nut holding the spout and metal sleeve in the faucet. Then turn off the spout which is threaded onto the faucet housing. Pad the wrench to prevent scratching the finish on the spout parts.

Slow-flow bathtub drains

Hair and clay-like soap residue usually is the problem with slow (or no) flowing tub and lavatory drains. Cleaning the stopper mechanism is the solution. Sink drains are easier than tub drains.

For sinks, trace the lever that controls the stopper below the sink. It will be a wire rod that connects to another rod that slips into the drain. The rod is held to the pipe with a knurled cap. Unscrew the cap and pull out the rod. You can now remove the stopper. Clean the stopper and reassemble the rod assembly in reverse order.

Some sinks and lavatories have a stopper twisted onto the rod. Untwist the stopper counterclockwise, clean it, and replace it on the rod. The replacement can be tricky, since the unsupported rod will slide out of alignment in the drain pipe. Try jiggling the stopper lever to re-align it so the stopper can be reconnected to the rod.

For bathtub drains, remove the strainer and unscrew the stopper from the rocker arm linkage.

Run water into the tub about ¼-inch deep. Then, with a plumber's suction cup, try to unblock the drain. Plug the overflow with a damp cloth, and use plenty of up/down action on the suction cup.

If this doesn't work, remove the escutcheon plate that holds the stopper trip lever. It is held by two screws. Then push aside the lever assembly. In this space, insert a flat drain auger or snake. The tip should go down through the opening until it is in the drainpipe under the top of the tub. Force the auger back-and-forth until you feel the debris block break.

HEIGHT ADJUSTMENT of a bathtub stopper is fixed by turning a nut. A spring at the other end of the linkage forces the stopper up or down. To remove the stopper, push it up with the trip lever and unscrew it.

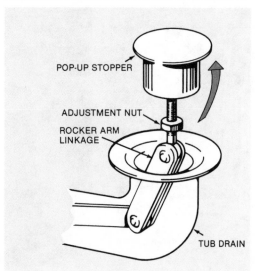

POP-UP STOPPER

ADJUSTMENT NUT

ROCKER ARM LINKAGE

TUB DRAIN

When a toilet runs constantly

The trouble usually is a worn tank ball, a pitted or worn tank-ball seat, or handle trip wires that don't properly release the tank ball so it drops solidly into the seat to shut off the water.

Take the lid off the flush tank. Then trip the handle and eyeball the wire linkage. If the wire is binding in the guides on the overfill pipe, turn the guide slightly on the pipe for alignment.

Tank balls often wear out, causing the ball to fill with water. Replace the ball. It is threaded to the lift wire which is connected to the linkage.

If the tank ball is worn where it fits into its metal seat at the bottom of the overfill tube, chances are that the seat is pitted or has a buildup of lime salts from water in the tank. Turn off the water at the supply or main valve; flush the toilet.

With medium steel wool, smooth the ball seat until it's shiny. If the seat is badly worn or pitted, you should replace the assembly.

Incomplete toilet flushes

An inadequate water supply in the flush tank can result in incomplete flushes. The solution to this problem is extremely simple.

Remove the flush tank lid. If the toilet has a floatarm/float ball assembly, try bending the float arm gently upward. Flush the toilet. The tank refill should come to about ¾-inch from the top of the overfill tube.

Some flushing devices are adjusted by turning a screw at the top of the float arm lever on the ballcock assembly. Low-profile ballcock models are adjusted by turning a knurled plastic screw at one end of the assembly at the top. These screws adjust the water height in the tank, which should be about 3–4 inches below the top edge of the flush tank.

Unclogging toilets the easy way

Any clogged toilet is messy to unclog. It is easier if you follow these procedures:

Do *not* flush the toilet. Remove any debris from the bowl by hand. Cover your hand and arm with several plastic garbage bags. You can get a grip through the plastic, although the material will restrict movement somewhat. With a dipper, remove as much water as possible from the bowl.

Seat a bulb-type plunger in the bowl, keeping the water line below the top of the plunger. Work the plunger up and down in the bowl. Use hard action on the plunger handle, but keep the rim of the plunger against the bowl surface. As you work you will feel the water moving in and out of the bowl. This vacuum breaks up the clog.

If the plunger doesn't work, try threading an auger with a hook on one end into the toilet trap. Crank the auger with its handle until the hook snags the clog. Then remove the clog on the end of the hook as you pull the auger out of the trap. To remove any remaining debris, flush the toilet several times.

BY REMOVING the overflow escutcheon, an auger or plumber's snake can be inserted into the drain pipe. Run the snake down the pipe until it makes the bend.

REMOVE the tank ball from its trip-handle linkage before you smooth the ball seat with steel wool. After cleaning you can see if the seat is pitted or worn, and needs replacing.

LOW WATER LEVEL is often the problem with incomplete toilet flushes. Try bending the float arm upward slightly. If there is water in the ball, the ball must be replaced.

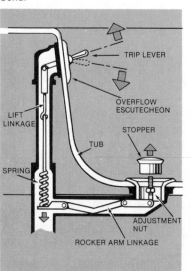

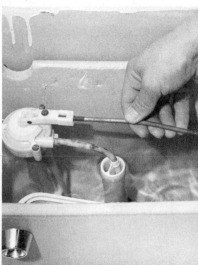

TRIP LEVER

OVERFLOW ESCUTCHEON

LIFT LINKAGE

STOPPER

TUB

SPRING

ADJUSTMENT NUT

ROCKER ARM LINKAGE

Leaks under the toilet bowl

Water on the floor around the bowl of a toilet doesn't necessarily mean the toilet bowl is cracked. The leakage most often is caused by a faulty wax seal between the bowl and waste stack. To replace the ring, you will have to lift the toilet bowl. The job is not as difficult as it might seem, although it is time consuming.

First, turn off the water supply to the toilet and flush the toilet. Dip out the water in the tank and bowl. Remove as much as you can.

Remove the flush tank from the toilet by removing the bolts through the bottom of the tank and into the back of the bowl. Also disconnect the supply line from the shutoff valve at the ball-cock assembly—not at the valve.

Two bolts usually hold the bowl to the floor. Remove these bolts (or nuts) with a wrench. If the fasteners are covered with ceramic caps, pry off the caps with a stiff-bladed putty knife or small prybar. The caps are usually set with plaster, or they are a snap-fit. You may have to clean the bolt threads before you can remove the bolts. If the bolts won't turn, saw them off with a hacksaw blade.

When the hold-down bolts are out, lift the bowl off the floor and tip it forward to trap the water inside the bowl. Then pour the excess water into the waste stack. Wipe the bowl clean.

At the top of the waste stack you will see what is left of a wax seal or ring. Under the seal will be a flange with two threaded bolts sticking out of it. If the bolts have been damaged, replace them and the flange. The cost is not prohibitive.

Since the toilet probably has been leaking for some time, the framing in the floor may be damaged. If so, cut short lengths of boards or dimension lumber to fit the width of the framing and spike these patches to the framing so they overlap the damage. What you're doing is reinforcing the

THE DEBRIS clogging a toilet seldom is in the water at the bottom of the bowl. It is in the toilet trap along the front of the bowl. Clean out all the debris you can see in the bowl, and dip out any excess water. Run a drum-type auger with a handle into the trap of the toilet. The hook on the end of the auger will snag any debris.

old framing with new wood. If the old framing is badly damaged and you can't patch it, call in a pro for repairs. The damaged wood may not support the weight of the toilet properly, causing serious problems later.

Put the new wax ring over the mounting flange at the top of the waste stack. Then slip the mounting bolts into the holes in the flange. The flange is slotted so the bolts may be moved for alignment. With a putty knife, smear setting compound around the top of the waste stack. Then set the bowl over the flange and thread the bolts through the base of the bowl. The toilet must seat on the floor for support—not on the wax ring.

When the bowl is firmly seated, tighten the holding nuts. Be careful; don't overtighten.

THE WAX SEAL—or ring—fits on the mounting flange. The flange is connected to the waste pipe. It's recommended that you replace the metal flange and bolts when you replace the wax ring. Have a helper seat the toilet over the flange as you align the bolts with the holes in the bottom of the toilet bowl. Keep the wax ring in the refrigerator until you install it. Heat will melt it.

A TOILET BOWL is fastened to a flange in the floor with two bolts. If the toilet has four bolts, the two front bolts usually are the flange bolts; the other two screw into the floor.

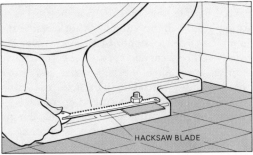

HACKSAW BLADE

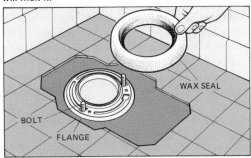

WAX SEAL

BOLT

FLANGE

Unclogging drains

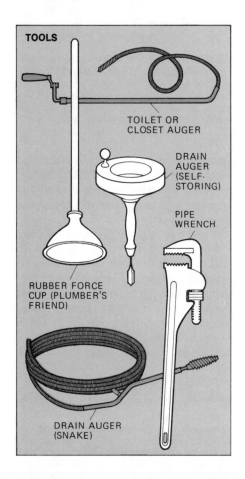

TOOLS

TOILET OR CLOSET AUGER

DRAIN AUGER (SELF-STORING)

PIPE WRENCH

RUBBER FORCE CUP (PLUMBER'S FRIEND)

DRAIN AUGER (SNAKE)

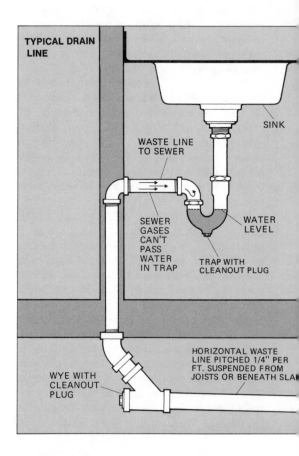

TYPICAL DRAIN LINE

SINK

WASTE LINE TO SEWER

SEWER GASES CAN'T PASS WATER IN TRAP

WATER LEVEL

TRAP WITH CLEANOUT PLUG

WYE WITH CLEANOUT PLUG

HORIZONTAL WASTE LINE PITCHED 1/4" PER FT. SUSPENDED FROM JOISTS OR BENEATH SLAB

Blocked drains—a common problem

Drain blockage (after dripping faucets) is probably the most frequently encountered home-plumbing problem. The first step to take when a drain has clogged is to check other drains in the house to determine whether the main waste line itself is blocked. A typical drain is shown above. Notice that between the sink basin and waste line horizontal run, there are two places where the line can be cleaned out—at the trap and at the wye. There should also be a cleanout at every angle (turn) in the waste line. The five tools shown above will let you handle most emergencies when the obstruction is in the fixture or reachable area of the waste line. If blockage is caused by tree roots outside, your best bet is to call in a pro with his equipment for clearing the line. To free a stopped-up sink, plug fixture's overflow vent and use a force cup. Remove stopper, cover force cup with water and stroke with up-and-down motion. Particles drawn up into sink should be removed and operation continued until line is running freely. If this doesn't work, try chemical cleaners; first scoop out all water in sink.

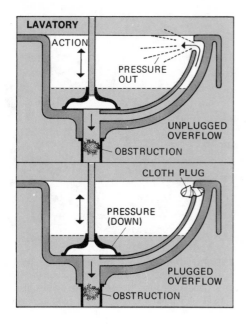

Clogged toilet

If just one toilet is clogged, it means that the problem is in the toilet itself and not in the drain line. Generally, a number of energetic thrusts with the force cup will free the obstruction. If this fails, try removing the obstruction using a bent wire coathanger or toilet auger. (Removal of the obstruction is better than pushing it along where it may clog further along the line.)

The toilet auger is a flexible wire encased in a metal tube. When the handle is cranked the flexible wire is forced out of the tube and into the trap. Though a good tool for clearing toilet obstructions, its effectiveness is limited by length—usually 3 to 4 ft. If the auger won't reach the obstruction, try using a drain and trap auger. If this fails, the toilet will have to be removed so clearing of line can be accomplished.

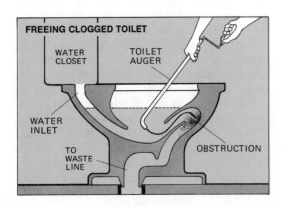

When all else fails

If you've tried all methods without success, the obstruction is in the main sewer line. In this event, a professional is required; with the tools and the specialized know-how for clearing clogged lines (usually tree roots) with a minimum of fuss and inconvenience for the family.

Chemical cleaners

To avoid clogged drains, chemical cleaners should be used at the first sign that water drainage is slowing down in fixtures. Make certain you read and follow the manufacturer's instructions on the container, paying particular attention to the safety precautions (and antidotes). When using chemical cleaners, wear rubber gloves, protect your eyes and make certain you *never use a force cup immediately after using chemicals;* your skin can be severely burned by liquids that may splash back. Give cleaner time to do its job (following maker's instructions), then flush out drain with cold water.

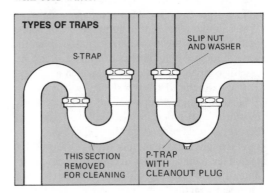

Cleaning out the trap

The primary function of the trap in a waste line is to prevent the odor of sewer gases from entering the house via the fixture. Water, which is always in the trap, prevents this from happening. If the force cup or chemicals won't clear the line, the third step is to clean out the trap. S-traps must be removed entirely for cleaning by loosening two slip nuts. However, most traps have a cleanout plug at the bottom. Here, simply place a pail beneath the trap and back out the cleanout plug. Then the obstruction usually can be washed out with tap water or snaked out with a drain auger. When line is clear, *carefully* replace the plug or slip nuts. They have very fine threads that are easily stripped if not started right. At this time, check washers on the slip nuts for resiliency. If they show signs of wear, they should be replaced.

All about pipe

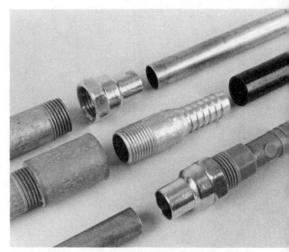

■ THE NOMINAL SIZE OF A PIPE is always determined by the inside diameter (i.d.). For example, a ¾-inch pipe will have a ¾-inch inside diameter or *approximately* a ¾-inch diameter. The actual size may vary slightly, but this is not important when buying pipe. Just ask for the nominal size you require. The standardized fittings and fixtures will fit the size that you specify.

The larger the pipe, the more water it delivers. Water supply pipes with a nominal size of ¾ to 1 inch (i.d.) are the workhorses that deliver the water directly to the fixtures or to a smaller pipe, usually copper or plastic tubing, which may have a ⅛- to ¼-inch (i.d.) nominal size.

Smaller-diameter pipes are adequate for sinks, lavatories and toilets, while the larger sizes are best for faucets such as outside sill cocks.

When buying pipes and fittings, be sure to match the metals: copper to copper, steel to steel, and so forth. Joining different metals causes a chemical reaction that can produce corrosion, rust, and eventually leaks. Two different-size pipes are joined with reducing fitting. The hookup between different types of pipe—copper-to-plastic, plastic-to-galvinized steel, etc.—is made with an adapter fitting, and it will be labeled as such in most stores.

Drain or waste pipe (DWV) also is measured by inside diameter, and the size may vary slightly. These pipes can be threaded, soldered, solvent-welded, clamped together with a gasket, or joined with lead, depending on the material from which they are manufactured.

Plumbing supplies are located in the plumbing departments of most stores, although DWV pipe and fittings may be located in the hard materials department (cement, sand) or the lawn and garden department. Pipes and fittings are displayed together so you can thread or push the fittings on various-size pipes to make sure you have the item you want.

The best way to shop for single repair products is to take the old part—pipe, fitting, washer, cartridge, gasket—to the store and match it. Second best is to measure exactly the part you want to replace and even make a rough sketch of it so the salesperson will know what you are after. If the part has a brand name jot this down, along with any other information that may be embossed on the part. The more information, the easier it is to find the right replacement.

If you are adding plumbing to an existing run—or replacing an existing run—always take a sketch plan of the installation to the store. The sketch doesn't have to be fancy, but it should include dimensions so you go home with the right parts. Also, the salesperson knows the business and may suggest plumbing shortcuts that will save you time and money.

Most home centers stock galvanized steel pipe, copper pipe, and copper tubing. Depending on plumbing codes in your community, the store may also stock plastic pipe.

DWV pipe, with the exception of plastic and a small selection of cast-iron fittings, may not be stocked by some retailers; you can find it at specialty plumbing stores. Special DWV pipe such as lead asbestos-cement seldom is stocked by home centers, but it is a regular item at plumbing supply shops.

Working with galvanized pipe

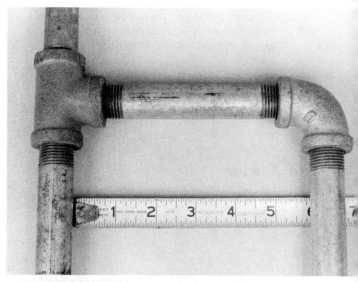

PIPE MEASUREMENTS are made from face-to-face between fittings plus the length of the threads that go into the fittings. For measuring pipe runs—where the pipe will go through walls and floors—figure from center-to-center between the pipe. Do this by measuring from one side of the pipe to the same side of the adjoining pipe. Center-to-center in this illustration would be 6¾ inches.

■ GALVANIZED STEEL PIPE is manufactured from steel, and galvanized to deter rust. A similar pipe is made for gas lines, but is colored black so you can tell the difference. Galvanized steel pipe costs less than copper; it is resistant to shocks such as blows from a hammer or other object. If your water supply is strongly alkaline, galvanized pipe will tend to accumulate lime and scale deposits, reducing the water flow.

Basic sizes of galvanized steel pipe, although not always readily available in all sizes, include ⅛, ¼, ⅜, ½, ¾, 1, 1¼, 1½, 2, and 2½ inches. All connections are threaded for necessary fitting or adaptors.

To assemble or disassemble galvanized steel pipe these tools are needed: two pipe wrenches, pipe cutter or hacksaw, a metal file, pipe reamer, cutting oil, and pipe joint compound. If you thread the pipe yourself, you will need a pipe die cutter and a vise. These two tools often can be rented.

Galvanized steel pipe is sold by size: diameter and length. Standard lengths in home centers and hardware outlets may be limited to 2, 4, 6, 10, and 12 feet, with both ends threaded to accept fittings. Longer lengths—up to 22 feet—usually are available at plumbing supply shops; these lengths may or may not be threaded.

Nipples are short lengths of galvanized steel pipes that measure from about 1½ to 12 inches long; nipples are threaded at both ends for fittings.

To determine the length of pipe needed, measure from the face (opening) of one fitting to the adjoining fitting. Add one inch to the overall dimension for pipe under one inch in nominal size; the threads turn into the fitting ½ inch at each end. If the pipe is from 1 to 2 inches in nominal size, add 1¼ inches to the overall dimension; the threads turn into the fitting ⅝ inch at each end.

Threads on galvanized steel pipe are slightly tapered. As the threads are turned into the fitting, the taper causes a tight fit between the pipe and fitting. Never overtighten fittings; overtightening can strip the threads or, worse, split the pipe or fitting.

Galvanized Steel Fittings

There are many different galvanized steel fittings available, but you probably will be concerned with only seven of them: 45° and 90° elbows, tees, reducing couplings, straight couplings, caps, and plugs. The fittings are threaded inside and/or outside to match the threads on the pipe. If you are adding copper or plastic pipe to an existing galvanized steel system, you will need a copper or plastic adaptor fitting. These adaptor fittings are usually located with the standard fittings.

Standard galvanized steel pipe fittings—elbows, couplings, tees, etc. turn *one* way. Therefore, when a pipe section is being repaired or a new section is being added to an existing section, a union fitting must be used so the pipe threads may be turned in the opposite direction. The union has three parts: two end pieces that screw into a common center. The end pieces have inside threads so the pipe may be connected like a straight coupling. Unions may be used almost anyplace along a plumbing run or section.

Threads on fittings are either male or female. Male threads are on the outside of the fitting; female threads are on the inside. Pipe joint compound or tape is placed on male threads to help prevent leaking after the pipe connections have been made. The compound, which is similar to putty, is smeared on the male threads in a thin coating. It may be purchased in a tube or can.

Plastic pipe tape is wrapped around the male threads before the connections to fittings are made. A couple of layers of the extremely thin ribbon is adequate.

How It's Sold.

Fittings are sold by the piece. If the fitting has more than one part to it, such as a union fitting, it is sold as a unit. Most galvanized steel fittings are not packaged so that you have an opportunity to try the fitting on the pipe.

Galvanized steel pipe and fittings are so commonplace that special-ordering it usually isn't necessary. If your regular retailer is out of stock on an item, you almost always will find it at another store.

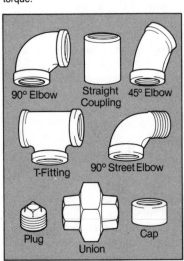

TWO PIPE WRENCHES should always be used in the assembly and disassembly of galvanized steel or threaded pipe. The jaws of the wrenches should be opposed, as shown here, for the proper turning pressure on the pipe and fitting. Go easy on the torque.

PLASTIC THREAD TAPE does the same job as joint compound—seals threads against leaks—but is less messy to use. It is available in several widths.

PIPE JOINT COMPOUND has the consistency of thin putty; it is smeared on the male threads of galvanized steel pipe before the pipe is turned into a fitting. The compound makes assembly easier and seals the threads to help prevent leaking.

GALVANIZED STEEL PIPE FITTINGS. The ones used most in plumbing repairs, shown here, are all manufactured in different sizes. Other specialized designs are stocked at home centers and hardware stores. Most repairs require a union fitting.

90° Elbow   Straight Coupling   45° Elbow

T-Fitting   90° Street Elbow

Plug   Union   Cap

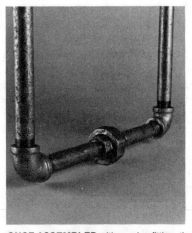

ONCE ASSEMBLED with a union fitting, the pipe run looks like this. One half of the fitting has been screwed into one piece of pipe. Then the outer ring is loosely screwed onto that half. The other half of the fitting is threaded onto the other piece of pipe and then into the ring. Then the entire assembly is tightened with two wrenches.

SADDLE TEE FITTING is used to quickly tap into a water supply pipe for a new water supply pipe, which can be galvanized steel, copper, or bronze. The water is first drained from the line, then a hole is drilled into the line, the tee is connected with a clamp and gasket, and finally the new line is connected.

90° ELL, CLOSE-ROUGH

90° STREET ELL, LONG RADIUS

RETURN BEND

BASEBOARD TEE

45° ELL

TEE

FITTING REDUCER

FITTING ADAPTER

COMPANION FLANGE NO. 125 STANDARD

CROSS

Working with copper pipe

■ COPPER PIPING is light and extremely durable, requires no threading of the ends to join it, comes in varying diameters, wall thicknesses and degrees of hardness, and is suitable for both hot and cold-water systems. To join copper piping, there are many types of fittings to cover every part of the plumbing layout. A number of common fittings are shown at the left.

Copper pipe can be joined using either soldered (also called capillary or "sweat" joints) or screwed (compression fitting) joints. Compression joints are of two types. With the first, called a "bead" fitting, the tubing is pushed into the fitting, a bead of jointing paste is applied around the tubing in front of a compression nut, and the compression nut is tightened onto the fitting. The result is a watertight fit. The second type is called a "flare" fitting because the end of the tubing is funnel-shaped with a special flaring tool (below). This shaped end receives the male end of the fitting; the compression nut is then tightened to finish the connection.

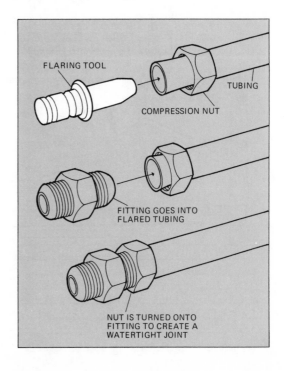

FLARING TOOL

TUBING

COMPRESSION NUT

FITTING GOES INTO FLARED TUBING

NUT IS TURNED ONTO FITTING TO CREATE A WATERTIGHT JOINT

Equipment needed

Propane torch
Hacksaw
Smooth file
Tubing bender
  (also known as
  a "hickey")

Tubing cutter
  with reamer
Sandpaper or fine
  steel wool
Solder
Flux

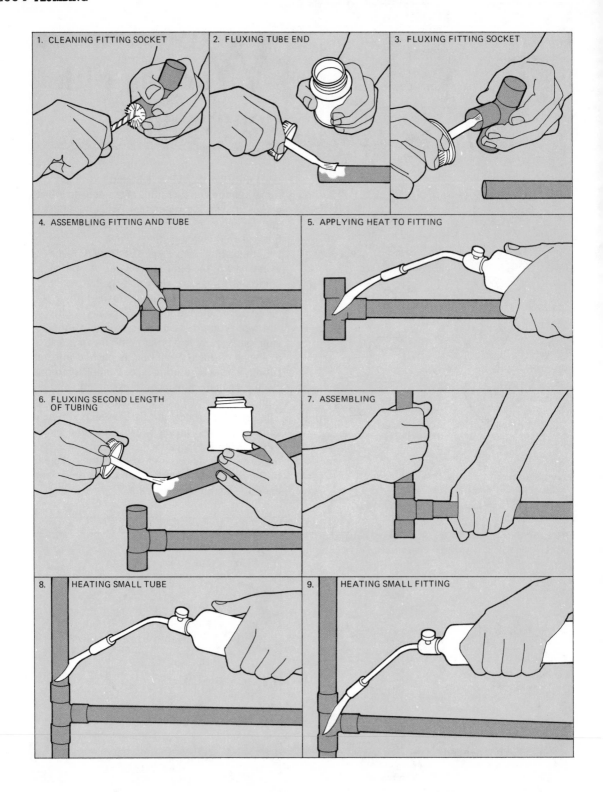

1. CLEANING FITTING SOCKET

2. FLUXING TUBE END

3. FLUXING FITTING SOCKET

4. ASSEMBLING FITTING AND TUBE

5. APPLYING HEAT TO FITTING

6. FLUXING SECOND LENGTH OF TUBING

7. ASSEMBLING

8. HEATING SMALL TUBE

9. HEATING SMALL FITTING

Soldering tips

Remember to align joints with adequate support before soldering, and to place no strain on them. When soldering, use torch with sweeping motion—tubing and fitting should be at same temperature for best flow of solder into joint. If solder forms lumps, joint is not hot enough. If there is no question that the joint is hot enough but solder still does not flow freely, overheating resulting in burned flux is likely, and the joint must be started again from Step 1. As soon as solder has set, use a wet brush or rag to crack and remove flux (remove it from inside of pipes by flushing with water); remove all flux before pressure-testing the joint—if necessary use a wire brush. If you have to redo a joint, reflux the entire joint area before applying heat to unsolder.

Cleaning copper piping

Clean the inside of the fitting with a wire brush. A thorough cleaning is absolutely necessary because a "sweat" joint relies on capillary action and *any* dirt, grease, or surface oxidation on the pipe or the fitting will hinder the joining action. Because the pipe should fit tightly into the fitting, do not remove too much metal when sanding or the capillary space will be enlarged and the joint weakened.

Assembling copper system

After you have thoroughly cleaned the inside of the fitting socket (Step 1), apply a thin coat of flux to the end of the pipe (Step 2) and the inside of the fitting (Step 3) with a small, clean brush. Then push the tubing tightly into the fitting (Step 4) and twist the pieces slightly in order to distribute the flux evenly. Wipe off any excess flux that remains and apply heat with a propane torch to the fitting (Step 5).

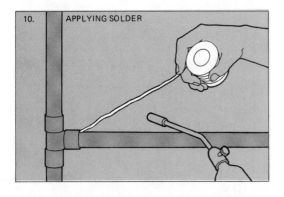

10. APPLYING SOLDER

In the same manner, apply flux to the second length of tubing (Step 6), insert in the fitting (Step 7) and apply a flame to both the tubing (Step 8) and fitting (Step 9). Melt the solder from a spool of soldering wire around the tubing-fitting joint (Step 10).

Flux for soldering is mildly corrosive. It contains zinc and ammonium chlorides in a petroleum base, and is used as a protective coating on the metal and as an agent to help the solder flow. Always stir flux before you use it.

The cardinal rule in choosing a solder is to buy a quality solder. Most solders for household plumbing jobs are composed of 50 percent tin and 50 percent lead. If the joint requires a solder of greater strength, use one comprising 95 percent tin and 5 percent antimony.

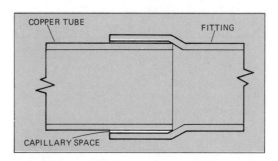

COPPER TUBE   FITTING

CAPILLARY SPACE

Capillary or 'sweat' joints

Properly prepared, a sweated joint will provide many years of troublefree (nonleaking) service. Although your joint may leak the first couple of times you attempt to sweat pipe, you'll soon be sweating copper pipe just like a pro by getting a little practice under your belt and by following the rules outlined on these pages.

To understand the principles of sweating pipe, you should understand how capillary action works. When the end of a copper pipe is inserted as far as possible into a fitting, a small amount of space will remain between the inside wall of the fitting and the outside wall of the pipe. When the fitting is heated with a propane torch and solder is applied around the pipe at the outer edges of the fitting, the solder will be drawn into this space by capillary action, bonding the pipe and fitting together securely. Such action will be the result regardless of whether the piping will be running horizontally or vertically.

If you're repairing or adding to an existing copper piping system, remember that all parts to be joined must first be completely dry. After the soldering is done and the joint cooled to room temperature, test the work for possible leaks.

Types of copper piping

Type	Temper
K	Hard (rigid) or soft (flexible)
L	Hard or soft
M	Hard only

To be sure the type of copper piping that you use for a specific application complies with local plumbing code, always check with your local building department. In general, Type L can be used below ground, Type M above ground. For a superior installation, use Type K below ground and Type L above ground.

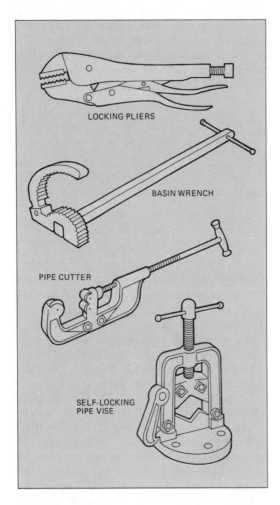

LOCKING PLIERS

BASIN WRENCH

PIPE CUTTER

SELF-LOCKING PIPE VISE

Toolbox additions

If you plan on doing most of your own plumbing jobs, the four tools shown can be valuable additions to your toolbox. The two pictured at the top are available at most hardware stores, while you may have to visit a plumbers' supply house to find the lower two.

Vise-grip pliers, with serrated jaws and locking nut, are especially useful when working with small-diameter pipes. A basin wrench, whose gripping head is adjustable, will save you many bumps and knocks on head and hands when you are installing a basin where there is little room for swinging ordinary wrenches.

A pipe cutter, which is faster and more accurate than a hacksaw when cutting iron or galvanized pipe, is operated simply by starting the cutter over the pipe, and, as it is revolved, tightening the handle gradually to deepen the cut. Thread-cutting oil should be applied to both the cutter and the pipe.

A self-locking pipe vise has V-shaped jaws that grip the pipe from both top and bottom. It eliminates the need for a helper to hold the pipe while you do the cutting.

Cutting and cleaning

Cut pipe to length using a tubing-cutter (1) or a fine hacksaw blade. Make sure the cut is square and the pipe remains round and true. Cutting with a hacksaw blade leaves rough edges on the inside and outside of the pipe, while a tubing cutter leaves rough edges on the inside of the pipe. Remove burrs on the outside of the pipe with a smooth file or sandpaper and on the inside with a reamer (2) or rattail file. Clean the end of pipe with steel wool or a strip of sandpaper (3).

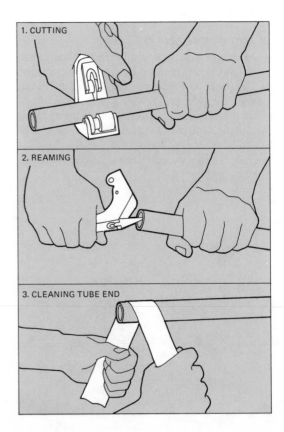

1. CUTTING

2. REAMING

3. CLEANING TUBE END

Working with plastic pipe

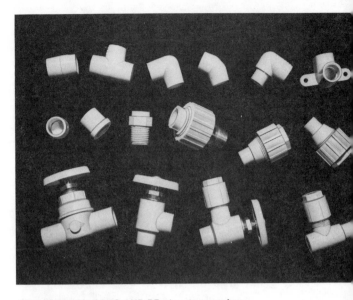

FITTINGS FOR CPVC AND PB pipe, top row from left: coupling, tee, 90° and 45° elbows, 90° street elbow, wing elbow. Center row: cap, reducing bushing, male thread adapter, transition union, two copper adapters. Bottom: line-shutoff valve, angle-shutoff valve, fixture shutoff valve and stackable tee.

■ SOME YEARS AGO, when copper tubing was the only smart choice for home water pipes, do-it-yourself plumbers enjoyed a complete system comprised of hard-temper (rigid) and soft-temper (flexible) copper. They could use the one that best suited their purpose—rigid pipe for neat-looking, exposed plumbing and flexible pipe for threading through walls and floors.

When rigid chlorinated polyvinyl chloride (CPVC) pipe was introduced, it made home plumbing a great deal easier, but didn't offer a system. Now, with the advent of flexible polybutylene (PB) pipe, plumbers again have the choice they had with copper, but at less cost and with far less effort. CPVC serves as the "hard-temper" and PB as the "soft-temper" thermoplastic pipe. Where one isn't best for a specific task, the other is.

Plastic pipe materials, usually beige in color are sold at hardware stores, home centers and wholesale plumbing outlets. Both CPVC and PB service hot and cold water and have a complete line of fittings. CPVC joins via simple solvent-welding. PB can't be solvent-welded, but joins with even greater ease using mechanical adapters, which solvent-weld to all standard CPVC fittings.

Both CPVC and PB can be cut with any fine-toothed saw. CPVC is usually sold in rigid, 10-ft. lengths with ½ and ¾-in. outside diameters. PB comes in 25 and 100-ft. coils with ⅜, ½ and ¾-in. outside diameters. According to a large manufacturer of thermoplastic piping, CPVC and PB pipes and fittings in these sizes are common.

Neither CPVC nor PB should be compared to lesser quality black polyethylene (PE) or polyvinyl chloride (PVC) pipe. PVC and PE should never be used inside a house for water supply; they can't stand up to household hot water.

Perhaps the chief reason for do-it-yourself use of CPVC/PB piping is its ease of installation. There's no more hand-tightening of pipe ends and no more sweat-soldering flames playing around your pipes. Solvent CPVC welding requires only a clean cloth, plus cans of cleaner and solvent. Joining PB requires even less—sandpaper and a little petroleum jelly.

Deciding which to use

CPVC, because it's rigid, runs off with the honors for appearance. It's best used where piping will be seen: in basements, unfinished utility rooms and garages. It's also useful where pipe must support a faucet, such as an outdoor hose bibb. Use CPVC for pipe sections requiring lots of fittings. CPVC fittings—like those for sweat-soldered rigid copper—are less costly than those for PB. Also, use CPVC elbows for within-wall turns in a run of PB where the PB can't bend as sharply as needed.

PB, because it's flexible, takes the cake for runs where pipe must be fed through bored holes. It's also ideal for long runs with gentle bends that are free of joints and fittings. This not only saves money, but cuts down on flow restrictions. It also reduces or eliminates measuring and cutting to fit complex runs around obstructions. A single, joint-free PB pipe can go through floors, around corners and wherever needed—in the ground, without joints. It's great beneath concrete slabs, too. Use PB to make runs you'll want to take apart easily at a later date. Adapters can be removed and reassembled as often as desired.

You can, but probably won't, use PB in exposed locations. Being flexible, it sags and doesn't look very neat. Also, for shorter runs, PB requires more fittings than are economical.

Another PB use is for flexible riser tubes. These reach from a water supply outlet on the wall or floor behind a fixture up to the faucet connections. PB riser tubes come as ⅜-in.-outside-diameter parts which you cut to length. They have factory-shaped ends. Riser tubes for sinks and lavatories are made with bullet-nosed ends to fit directly into most faucet tailpipes. They're held in place by a faucet nut, also called a jam nut. Riser tubes for toilets are flange-ended to connect into the toilet's inlet valve with a jam nut. PB risers are so flexible they reach from outlet to faucet easily without kinking. Cut them to length with a pocket knife.

Advantages of plastic pipe

Both CPVC and PB are also energy savers. Their walls pass heat much less rapidly than metal. Hot water stays hot longer and cold water pipes sweat less. The smooth walls of CPVC and PB offer less resistance to water flow, enabling smaller sizes to do the same job as larger steel pipes.

A CPVC/PB system won't corrode and won't conduct electricity, making it free from electrolysis that eats away at metal pipes. One disadvantage here is that your water system can't be used as an electrical ground.

Both CPVC and PB meet practically all building codes. CPVC conforms to ASTM Standard D-2846; PB to ASTM Standard D-3309. Both are accepted by the Federal Housing Administration and meet all requirements for potable water by the National Sanitation Foundation. They both take 100 lbs. p.s.i. continuous pressure at 180° F. However, before undertaking any plumbing project, you should verify that all procedures and materials meet local codes.

Tips for an expert installation

CPVC pipes and fittings join together by solvent-welding (see photos). Besides using a liberal amount, it's important to use a high-quality solvent containing lots of tetra hydrofuran, a high-

cost but effective ingredient of good solvent cements. PB pipe can't be solvent-welded, so don't try. To join PB to CPVC, solvent-weld the CPVC to one end of an adapter, and, after applying petroleum jelly, simply hand-tighten the PB to the other end.

CPVC or PB can be joined directly to threaded metal pipe and fittings or to unthreaded copper pipe. This is also a simple task, but requires special adapters, called transition unions. You'll need them for appliance outlets and inlets, at threaded faucets and when using plastic to extend an existing system of metal pipe.

Transition unions mate up metal and thermoplastic piping across an elastomeric rubber gasket. They permit differential thermal movement between the two materials without straining the parts. They also prevent the leaking associated with ordinary threaded adapters.

Transition unions come in male and female threads for metal pipes and fittings and can also be sweat-soldered to unthreaded copper. CPVC solvent-welds directly to transition unions, but a transition union *and* an adapter are needed to join PB to metal, because PB can't be solvent-welded.

Use transition unions at every pressurized hot water connection between threaded metal and solvent-welded plastic piping. At nonpressurized hot water and at cold water connections, use simple male thread adapters, if possible. Transition unions can be taken apart and reassembled without cutting pipes.

With all water supply piping, but especially with thermoplastic, you must allow for pipe expansion and guard against overpressure or excessive temperatures. When installing CPVC pipe, always use special hangers that let the pipe slide back and forth without binding, yet hold it securely to the framing. Leave room for expansion at the ends of long runs of CPVC, generally allowing ¼ in. for each 10 ft. of pipe. Install doglegs—offsets—in CPVC runs of more than 35-ft., and where risers reach up from water mains through the floor. Make sure offsets are at least 8 in. long to permit slight end-wise movement. With 'PB risers, forget this precaution. Use PB wherever possible on long runs; it's so flexible, it's not harmed by expansion or contraction.

To control high temperature in the system, install 8 to 11-in. threaded nipples atop the tank of your gas or oil-fired water heater before putting in transition unions to connect piping. Nipples keep conducted heat from the plastic piping. They aren't necessary on an electric heater.

FOR A NEAT, craftsmanlike look where plumbing shows—as in this basement—use rigid CPVC piping.

WHEN PIPING must be fitted behind walls or fished through openings, use flexible PB to save time and effort.

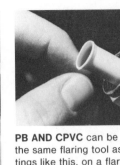

PB AND CPVC can be joined by using the same flaring tool as for copper. Fittings like this, on a flared riser tube, join PB to uncommon fixtures.

CPVC AND PB adapt to other pipes. From top, CPVC/FIP (female thread) transition union joins CPVC to male-threaded bibb; a compression union joins copper to the PB tubing; a special adapter connects the solderless joint with copper tubing; CPVC connects to the threaded brass pipe via a flare-reducing adapter.

TRANSITION UNIONS connect CPVC to tub/shower mixing valve. Unions solvent-weld to CPVC or to push-in adapters, preventing leaks from thermal expansion.

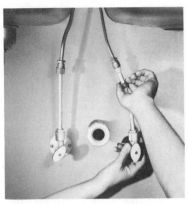

USE superflexible PB riser tubes between all types of fixture shutoff valves and faucet tailpipes. Tubes seal the inside threaded fittings.

IDEAL COMBINATION: rigid CPVC pipes look tidy in basement while flexible PB riser tubes simplify runs to fixtures. Combination saves much cutting and fitting.

PB CAN BE used beneath a concrete slab. Install joint-free runs. Then attach any fixtures to the exposed pipe ends located above the slab.

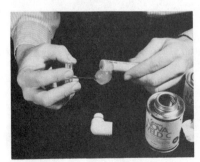

TO JOIN plastic pipe to fitting, remove burrs from cut end with knife and apply the cleaner-primer. Apply solvent cement using swab from can.

IMMEDIATELY after applying the cement, join the pieces with a twisting motion. Quickly orient fitting because solvent dries rapidly. Wipe off excess.

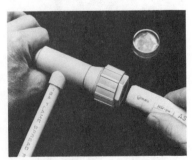

TO JOIN PB to PB, CPVC or metal pipe, use an adapter that hand-tightens. Cut tube end even (use miterbox), round corners and coat with petroleum jelly.

WHERE TO USE CPVC AND PB

LOCATION	CPVC	PB	3/4"	1/2"	3/8"
Service entrance		1	•		
House mains:					
Basement	1		•		
Crawlspace		1			
Beneath slab		1			
Fixture branches	3	2		•	
Riser tubes		1			•
Below ground to outbuildings		1	•	•	
To outdoor hose bibbs	2	3	•	•	
Water softener	3	2	•		
Water heater	2	2	•		
T & P valve relief tube	2	3		•	
Air chambers	1		•	•	
Automatic washer hose bibbs	2	3		•	
Showerhead riser pipe	1			•	
Furnace humidifier		1			•
Boiler inlet connection*	2	3		•	
Evaporative cooler		1		•	•
Lawn sprinkler supply*	3	2	•	•	•
Piping of manifolds		1		•	•
Behind finished walls		1	•	•	•
Sharp turns within walls	1			•	•
Gentle turns		1	•	•	•
Around obstructions		1	•	•	•
Long, joint-free runs		1		•	•
Short runs, many connections	1			•	•

* With approved backflow preventer   1—Best   2—Better   3—Good

THERMOPLASTIC PIPE CONNECTIONS AT WATER HEATER

FROM COLD WATER MAIN
3/4" CPVC PIPE (OR PB)
3/4" CPVC COUPLING
LINE STOP VALVE
TO HOT WATER MAIN
8" TO 11" METAL NIPPLES TAKE BURNER'S CONDUCTED HEAT (NOT NEEDED ON ELECTRIC HEATER).
3/4" FIP-CPVC TRANSITION UNIONS
3/4" CPVC ELBOW
T & P VALVE
3/4" MALE ADAPTER
3/4" CPVC PIPE
WATER HEATER
TO FLOOR DRAIN

To control excessive pressure caused by water action within the piping system, put an air chamber at each fixture. You can make one by simply adding a capped 12-in. length of ½-in.-outside-diameter CPVC pipe to a tee behind the wall at the fixture. If the pipe serves an automatic-shut-off appliance like a washer, use a ¾-in.-outside-diameter pipe 18 in. long.

Locate a stop-and-drain valve so the whole system can be turned off and drained to prevent freeze-up. While PB isn't damaged even by repeated freezing and CPVC can take a number of freeze-ups, their fittings cannot. Of course, the cold water inlet to the water heater should contain a valve. A line stop (shutoff) valve is handy for this. One type solvent-welds either to ½-in. pipe *inside* the hubs or to ¾-in. pipe fittings *outside* the hubs. A pair of ¾-in. couplings make it serve a run of ¾-in. pipe.

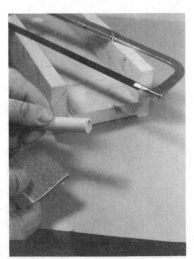

REMOVE ALL BURRS with a file after cutting plastic pipe absolutely square with a hacksaw. The end of the pipe must fit squarely inside the fitting.

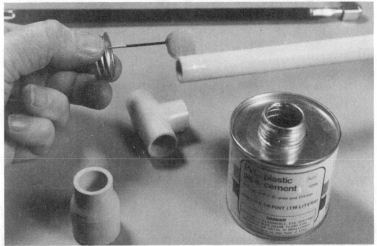

PLASTIC PIPE IS ASSEMBLED with a specific cement that forms a solvent weld. Before the cement is applied, however, dry-assemble the pipe to make sure that it fits satisfactorily. Once solvent-welded, the pipe can not be disassembled at the welds; it must be cut.

Relocate a toilet

■ IF YOU DECIDE to remodel your old bath and think the toilet will work out better else-where, then follow these steps to move it. If you're adding a new bath or powder room to your house, the same basic approach works for new toilet installation as well.

How a toilet works

Most toilets are one of two basic types: a low-profile one-piece unit and a higher two-piece unit that has a wall-mounted water tank connected to the bowl by an elbow. Both work on the same basic principle: water enters the storage tank from the house cold water supply line through a valve that is activated by a ball float inside the tank. When the toilet is flushed, the water goes into the bowl, carries out the waste and leaves behind enough water in the bottom of the bowl to create an airtight seal between the waste line and the room. This prevents sewer gases from escaping into your house. To move the toilet, you must move the fixture, the water supply line and the waste line.

Removing the water lines and fixture

Start by shutting off the water below the external shutoff valve beneath the storage tank. In some cases there will be a valve in the basement located in the toilet supply line. Often this is omitted because of the shutoff valve directly below the water tank. If that is the case, you'll have to turn off the supply of water to the entire house while doing the job, or install a temporary shutoff valve below the bathroom.

Flush the toilet to remove the water in the tank, then sponge out the tank and the bowl to remove the standing water left behind. Remove the hanger bolts under the caps on the side of the toilet base.

Using adjustable wrenches or small pipe wrenches, remove the shutoff valve and supply line directly below the water tank. Then lift the bowl off the floor flange and set it to one side. With a two-piece toilet, you'll have to loosen the elbow that connects the tank to the bowl and then lift the tank from the wall before moving the bowl.

Once the bowl is free, the floor flange will be exposed as shown. Cut the pipe below the flange using a hacksaw and remove the flange from the floor.

BEGIN BY TURNING OFF the house water supply at the water meter. A valve should be on either the main side (above) or house side.

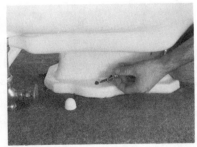

LIFT OFF COVER CAPS, then remove hanger bolts (above, on older toilets) or nuts on hold-down bolts (on newer units).

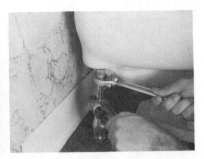

MAKE SURE that all water is sponged from the interior of the storage tank, then remove the supply line and shutoff valve.

ESTABLISH A CENTERLINE for the toilet's new position and draw it on the floor using a framing square against the room wall.

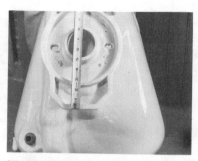

STAND THE BOWL on end and measure the distance from the back of the bowl's base to the edge of its outlet horn (center hole).

CENTER THE BOWL over the floor line, then push it against the wall with a piece of wall finish material held between the two.

MAKE SURE THE BOWL is square to the wall and centered over the floor line. Outline the entire base perimeter on the floor.

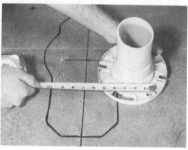

MOVE THE BOWL away and mark the centerpoint of the outlet horn on the floor. Then measure the diameter of the waste flange.

DRAW A CIRCLE for the waste flange on the floor, centered over the cross-hatch marks. Bore a blade entry hole on its perimeter.

CUT THE WASTE FLANGE HOLE using a key hole, sabre or reciprocating saw. Make sure there are no wires or water pipes below the cut.

PLACE THE WASTE FLANGE in the hole and make sure it seats flat on the floor. Note how the joist side was cut slightly for fit.

ALIGN THE FLANGE on your new flooring so the hold-down bolt slots face to the sides. Attach with screws driven into the floor.

SLIDE THE HOLD-DOWN BOLTS into the flange slots so both are parallel to the room wall. The slots have room for precise adjustment.

PRESS A NEW WAX SEAL, smooth side up, onto the flange. It should fit just between the bolts and be centered over the waste hole.

LOWER THE BOWL into place so the side holes slide over the bolts. Push down to flatten the seal, then install washers and nuts.

BEGIN FABRICATING the new waste line by cutting lengths of 3-in.-dia. plastic pipe to size. Use a hacksaw and make square cuts.

TO JOIN ANY FITTING to the pipe, first wipe the pipe end and fitting seat with solvent and a soft cloth until both are clean.

NEXT, APPLY PLASTIC WELDING CEMENT to the mating surfaces of the pipe and fitting using the applicator that comes with the can.

SLIDE THE FITTING over pipe and push until the pipe is seated. Then turn fitting ¼ turn to make sure cement spreads evenly.

TEST-FIT PREASSEMBLED SECTION between the flange and the waste line. Then clean and cement both end joints at the same time.

TAP INTO YOUR EXISTING COLD WATER LINE by removing a section of iron pipe, as shown, or by cutting through a copper line.

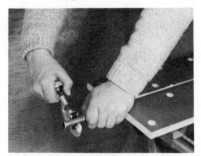

USE COPPER TUBING instead of iron pipe for the new supply line. For best results, cut it to length using a tubing cutter.

ONCE THE TUBING IS CUT, and the burrs removed from the inside of the pipe, clean the end with steel wool until it shines brightly.

USING YOUR FINGER, apply a generous amount of soldering flux to the end of the tubing. When heated, the flux helps clean the pipe.

Prepare the new floor

Prepare your new floor. You may have to replace subflooring over the hole of the old toilet location. Install a hardboard underlayment to provide a smooth surface for your flooring. Locate the new position for the toilet by marking a centerline on the new flooring using a framing square. Then slide the bowl against the wall so the base is centered over this line. Mark the entire perimeter of the base.

Measure from the back—or front—of the bowl base to the waste hole on the bottom of the fixture. If you plan to install wainscoting, or even drywall, be sure to hold a piece of the material between the toilet and wall before you make your marks. Mark the center of the waste hole on the floor, and draw a circle the diameter of the flange. Cut the hole after you've made sure there are no water pipes or electrical wires beneath the floor.

Install the new flange

Once the hole is cut, attach the flange over the finished flooring by screwing it in place. Make

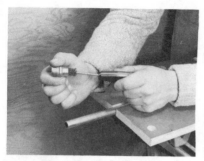

THE INSIDE OF EACH FITTING must be as clean as the tubing end. Use steel wool, emery cloth or the inexpensive wire brush shown.

ALSO APPLY SOLDERING FLUX to the inside of each fitting—in this case a male pipe thread adapter—and slide it over the tubing end.

USING A PROPANE TORCH, heat the joint with the tip of the inner blue flame. When hot enough, the solder will melt into the joint.

ALLOW THE PIPE to cool for several minutes—or dip it in water—then cover threads on the adapter with joint compound.

THREAD THE COPPER pipe and adapter assembly into the iron pipe supply line and tighten it securely with an adjustable wrench.

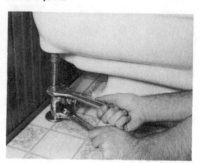

REINSTALL THE SHUTOFF VALVE and join it to the toilet tank with its extension nipple and compression fitting. Turn on the water.

sure the slots in the flange that receive the hold-down bolts are positioned on the sides of the flange. There is some adjustment for the bolts in these slots to achieve precise alignment later.

Attach the flange to the house waste system from below the floor. Depending on your local plumbing code, and where you place the toilet, this job can be very simple or much more complicated. In the installation shown, the toilet was less than 6 ft. away from the main house stack—the larger diameter vent you see on the top of house roofs. Therefore, it was necessary only to run a length of 3-in.-dia. plastic pipe from an old tee in the stack and to the flange. If, however, the flange is much farther from the main house vent, you will have to run another stack up through the roof so the system is vented properly. Consult your local building department before proceeding. Also keep in mind that horizontal runs of waste line should be pitched down ¼ in. for every foot of run toward the sewer outlet.

Install supply lines

Once the waste line is hooked up, install the new cold water supply line to the toilet's water tank. As with waste lines, the supply line should be pitched slightly down from the fixture it supplies—about ¼ in. for every 4 ft. of horizontal run. This is required so the system can be drained completely from a single low point.

Extend the new supply line to the toilet using a variety of copper fittings. Then bore a hole through the bathroom floor just below the supply hole in the water tank. In most new construction the supply line comes out of the wall behind the tank. This allows the bathroom floor to be cleaned without obstruction.

Install the fixture

Next, place a new wax seal over the waste flange as shown and lower the toilet onto the seal. Make sure the hold-down bolts protrude through the base holes. Then rock the bowl back and forth slightly to flatten the seal. Install washers over the bolts, tighten the nuts and cover with porcelain or plastic covering caps. Reinstall the shutoff valve and supply line above it, then turn on the water and immediately check for any leaks in the supply line. Finally, flush the toilet and check for leaks in the waste line.

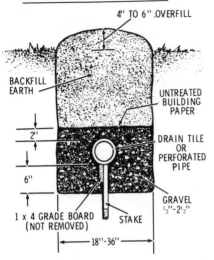

CROSS SECTION OF DISPOSAL LINE

4" TO 6" OVERFILL

BACKFILL EARTH

UNTREATED BUILDING PAPER

DRAIN TILE OR PERFORATED PIPE

2"

6"

GRAVEL ½"-2½"

1 x 4 GRADE BOARD (NOT REMOVED)

STAKE

18"-36"

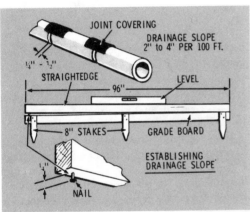

JOINT COVERING

DRAINAGE SLOPE 2" to 4" PER 100 FT.

¼" - 1½"

STRAIGHTEDGE

LEVEL

96"

8" STAKES

GRADE BOARD

ESTABLISHING DRAINAGE SLOPE

1"

NAIL

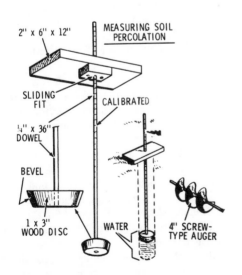

MEASURING SOIL PERCOLATION

2" x 6" x 12"

SLIDING FIT

CALIBRATED

¼" x 36" DOWEL

BEVEL

1 x 3" WOOD DISC

WATER

4" SCREW-TYPE AUGER

Septic system that's trouble-free

■ TROUBLE-FREE OPERATION of a septic-tank disposal system depends, first of all, on good design, adequate size and proper installation. Of equal importance is the volume of waste discharged into the system, and how often the tank is inspected and emptied.

Most communities require strict compliance with local ordinances in granting a permit for a disposal system and approving its installation. Therefore, when planning one, first acquaint yourself fully with local regulations.

How system works. In a typical septic-tank disposal system, waste entering the tank decomposes in liquid that normally fills the tank up to the outlet. Part of the waste settles to the bottom forming sludge, and part of it floats on the liquid forming scum. Only the clear liquid, called "effluent," should pass through the outlet. The purpose of a septic tank is to condition the effluent for absorption in the soil. When sewage enters the tank, an equal volume of the effluent passes into the disposal lines to soak into the earth within about 36 in. from the surface. Disease-producing bacteria in the effluent are eliminated here.

Location requirements. The septic tank and disposal field must be located at safe distances from sources of water supply. In general, the distance should not be less than 50 ft. for the septic tank and 100 ft. for the disposal field. Both should be on the downhill side of the water supply source, since ground pollution moves in the same direction as ground water.

A septic tank should be at least 5 ft. from any building. The disposal field should be located in an open area at least 10 ft. from buildings; about 15 ft. from property lines; about the same from trees and dense shrubbery (to avoid root troubles); and 25 ft. from streams or lakes.

Neither septic tank nor disposal field should be located in a swampy area or one subject to frequent flooding. The maximum height of ground water should be at least 4 ft. below ground level. Rock strata and other impervious formations should be at least 4½ ft. below disposal lines. You can check for all of this with a 2-in. earth auger fitted with extensions.

Soil porosity. When planning a septic-tank disposal system, the first thing to do is to test soil porosity. Use a 4-in. soil auger to make 6 or 8 holes about as deep as the disposal trenches are

If there is no water in the hole, fill it to a 6-in. depth and measure the drop at 30-min. intervals over a period of 4 hrs., refilling as necessary and using the last check. In soils where the first 6 in. of water seeps away in less than 30 min., measure the drop every 10 min. over a period of 1 hr. and use the last check. Refer to Table A for the

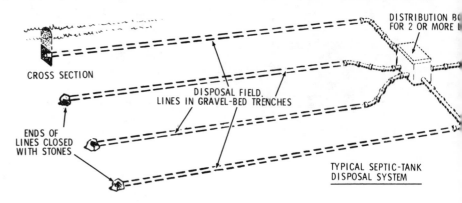

CROSS SECTION

ENDS OF LINES CLOSED WITH STONES

DISPOSAL FIELD. LINES IN GRAVEL-BED TRENCHES

DISTRIBUTION BOX FOR 2 OR MORE LINES

TYPICAL SEPTIC-TANK DISPOSAL SYSTEM

to be, space them uniformly over the selected site. Scrape the sides and bottoms of the holes with a knife to eliminate smeared surfaces and remove loose earth. Place a 2-in. layer of gravel or coarse sand on the bottom.

Keep the holes filled with water overnight and make percolation tests 24 hrs. after water was first put into the holes. (The percolation rate is the time required for water to drop 1 in.) If water is still present, adjust its depth to 6 in. and measure the drop in level over 30-min. periods, using the last check to figure the percolation rate.

needed length of the disposal field per bedroom in the dwelling it is to serve. If the soil has a percolation rate slower than 1 in. in 60 min., it is not suitable for a disposal field. In such cases the local health authority should be consulted for recommendations.

Disposal field. Most disposal fields consist of trenches in which drain tile or perforated, non-metallic pipe is laid in gravel. Only this type of disposal area will be discussed here. Trenches should not be less than 18 in. nor more than 36 in. in either depth or width. The depth is influenced by septic-tank outlet and ground slope.

A single line should not exceed 100 ft. in length. Parallel lines should be spaced as in Table B. If there are two or more lines, a distribution box is needed to control the flow uniformly. It may be prefabricated or cast in concrete on the site. The outlets are at equal level just above the bottom. The cover should be removable, sealed and at least 8 in. below ground level. The pipe line from the septic tank to the distribution box and also those from the distribution box to the separate disposal lines should be soil pipe with leakproof joints. A gravel bed under this pipe is unnecessary but the pipe should have the same drainage slope as the disposal lines.

After the trenches are dug, 1 x 4 grade boards on which pointed stakes are nailed are located centrally in the trenches. The upper edge should be about 6 in. above the trench bottom and should have a drainage slope of ¼ in. per 8 lin. ft. The bottoms of the trenches are raked to a

TABLE A RECOMMENDED SIZE OF DISPOSAL-FIELD TRENCHES				
PERCOLATION RATE — (MIN. WATER FALLS 1")	LINEAL FEET OF TRENCH PER BEDROOM			
	WIDTH 18" DEPTH 19"-30"	WIDTH 24" DEPTH 19"-30"	WIDTH 30" DEPTH 19"-30"	WIDTH 36" DEPTH 24"-36"
2 OR LESS	57	43	34	28
3	67	50	40	33
4	77	58	46	38
5	84	63	50	42
10	110	83	66	55
15	127	95	76	63
30	167	125	100	83
60	220	165	132	110

OVER 60—NOT SUITABLE FOR DISPOSAL TRENCHES. NOTE—MINIMUM TRENCH LENGTH IS FOR 2 BEDROOMS.

TABLE B DISTANCE BETWEEN TRENCHES	
TRENCH WIDTH	FEET DISTANCE BETWEEN CENTERLINES
12" TO 18"	6'
18" TO 24"	6½'
24" TO 30"	7'
30" TO 36"	7½'

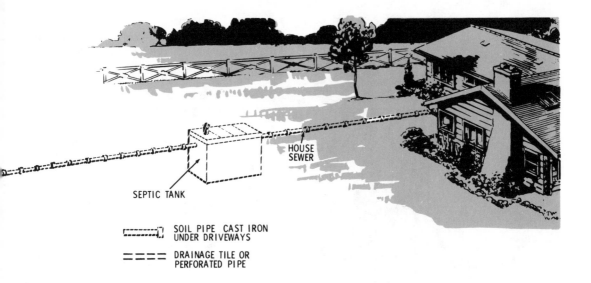

HOUSE
SEWER

SEPTIC TANK

⌐----⌐ SOIL PIPE CAST IRON
        UNDER DRIVEWAYS
==== DRAINAGE TILE OR
        PERFORATED PIPE

depth of 1 in. to eliminate smeared and com-
pacted earth which interferes with absorption.
Gravel or crushed stone (½ in. to 2½-in.) is laid
on the bottom up to the top edge of the grade
boards, which remain in place.

Next, 4-in. drain tile, or perforated pipe with

holes down, is placed centrally on the boards
while more gravel is added on either side and on
top, enough to cover the pipe to a depth of at
least 2 in. Joints between drainage tile should be
open from ¼ in. to ½ in., and the top of each joint
is covered with a piece of asphalt-impregnated

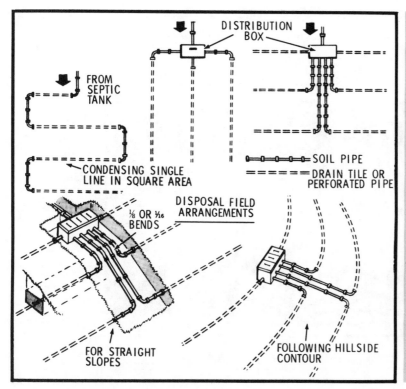

DISTRIBUTION
BOX

FROM
SEPTIC
TANK

CONDENSING SINGLE
LINE IN SQUARE AREA

⌐--- SOIL PIPE
==== DRAIN TILE OR
        PERFORATED PIPE

DISPOSAL FIELD
ARRANGEMENTS

⅛ OR ¹⁄₁₆
BENDS

FOR STRAIGHT
SLOPES

FOLLOWING HILLSIDE
CONTOUR

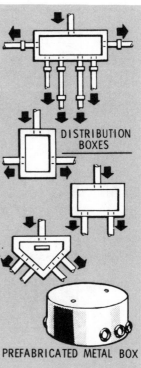

DISTRIBUTION
BOXES

PREFABRICATED METAL BOX

WHEN A SEPTIC TANK is cast on the site, the walls and bottom should be at least 6 in. thick and reinforced. Also, the inner surfaces must be completely waterproofed.

paper or a sheet-metal cover. After the gravel is smoothed, it is covered with untreated building paper, or with a 2-in. layer of straw or hay. When refilling the trench, pile up a mound of earth 4 in. to 6 in. high to allow for settling, so no depression will form along the trench line.

For sloping grades the disposal lines are laid at right angles to the direction of the slope if it is straight. Otherwise, the lines follow the ground contour. *A driveway should not be laid over any portion of the disposal field.* Drainage tile may be crushed by the weight of heavy vehicles. If the disposal field is on one side of a driveway and the septic tank on the other, the two should be connected with cast-iron pipe.

Septic tank: This may be a prefabricated steel tank suitably coated to prevent rusting; a prefabricated concrete tank having reinforced walls not less than 2½ in. thick; a concrete tank, cast on the site, having 6-in. reinforced walls and bottom; or a tank made of concrete blocks. The inside surfaces of the latter two should have a ¼-in.-thick coating of 1:2 portland cement-sand plaster, or other effective waterproofing.

Table C gives the required capacities of septic tanks based on the number of bedrooms. (The capacity of a tank is the volume below the liquid

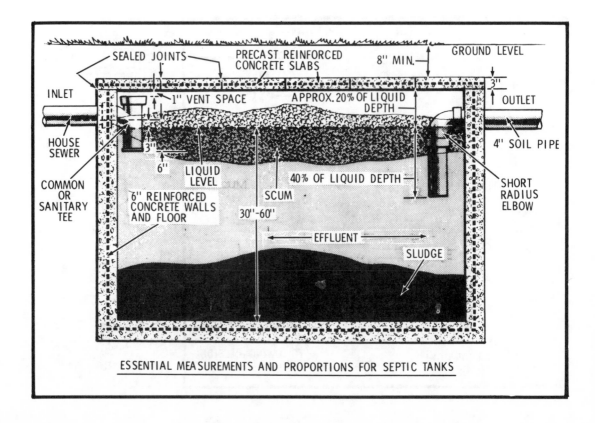

ESSENTIAL MEASUREMENTS AND PROPORTIONS FOR SEPTIC TANKS

TABLE C RECOMMENDED SIZE FOR SEPTIC TANKS					
INCLUDES ALLOWANCE FOR GARBAGE GRINDER, AUTOMATIC WASHERS AND OTHER APPLIANCES					
NUMBER OF BEDROOMS	MINIMUM CAPACITY (GALS.)	RECTANGULAR TANK SIZE (FT)			
		WIDTH INSIDE	LENGTH INSIDE	DEPTH INSIDE	LIQUID DEPTH
2 OR LESS	750	3½	7½	5	4
3	900	3½	8	5½	4½
4	1,000	4	8	5½	4½
5	1,250	4	9	5½	4½
(1 CU. FT. VOLUME EQUALS 7.48 GALS.)					

level.) These capacities allow for the disposal from garbage grinders, automatic washers and other common household appliances. It is best to have a tank that exceeds requirements, however, as fewer cleanings then will be necessary, which reduces maintenance cost.

A septic tank must be watertight. Cover slabs of 3-in. reinforced concrete are sealed with asphalt mastic or cement mortar to prevent the entrance of water or escape of gas. No vent is needed on the tank as the soil-pipe stack of the house serves this purpose.

The shape of a septic tank, whether square, rectangular or cylindrical, is of little importance. The top of the closed tank should come at least 8 in. below ground level. The outlet is provided with a tee, elbow or baffle extending below the liquid surface a distance of about 40 percent of its depth, for tanks having vertical sides, and about 35 percent for cylindrical tanks installed horizontally. For the former, the distance from the inside of the top to the liquid surface should be about 20 percent of the liquid depth, and for the latter this distance should be about 15 percent. The inlet should be at least 1 in. above the liquid surface, and preferably 3 in. A tee or baffle is provided to extend about 6 in. below the liquid surface to assure minimum disturbance from entering sewage. The upper end of the tee or baffle should be about 1 in. below the tank top to permit gas in the tank to escape through the house stack.

A single-compartment tank will give entirely satisfactory results, although a two-compartment tank (or two tanks connected) will be slightly more efficient. If a disposal system becomes too small to meet increased requirements, a second tank can be added and the size of the disposal field increased. The depth of the house sewer is determined after a septic tank has been installed. This pipe should have a cleanout opening at the house.

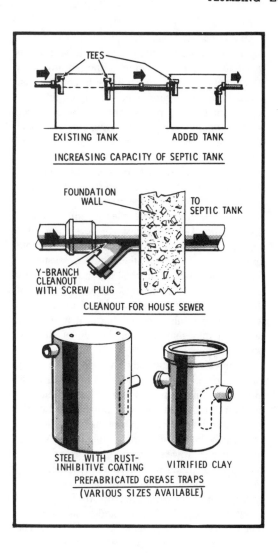

INCREASING CAPACITY OF SEPTIC TANK

EXISTING TANK ADDED TANK

TEES

CLEANOUT FOR HOUSE SEWER

FOUNDATION WALL

TO SEPTIC TANK

Y-BRANCH CLEANOUT WITH SCREW PLUG

PREFABRICATED GREASE TRAPS (VARIOUS SIZES AVAILABLE)

STEEL WITH RUST-INHIBITIVE COATING VITRIFIED CLAY

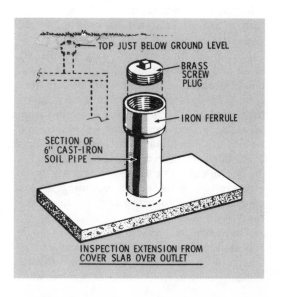

INSPECTION EXTENSION FROM COVER SLAB OVER OUTLET

TOP JUST BELOW GROUND LEVEL

BRASS SCREW PLUG

IRON FERRULE

SECTION OF 6" CAST-IRON SOIL PIPE

Maintenance: When first put into operation a septic tank does not require an additive such as yeast to start fermentation, although this may accelerate it. Septic-tank systems in constant use seldom freeze. Where winter temperatures are exceptionally low, protection can be provided with an adequate layer of straw, hay or snow. When the system is out of service for a period of time it is more susceptible to freezing. Clogging of disposal lines by roots occurs mostly in lines not having enough gravel under them. Usually the roots concentrate in the gravel.

Soaps, detergents, bleaches, drain cleaners, disinfectants, fat, oil, grease, the discharge of a garbage grinder and of other common household appliances connected to the plumbing system— none of these will, in normal amounts, have any adverse effects on septic-tank disposal systems of the sizes given in the tables. Waste brines from water softeners also are not harmful in a septic tank, but they may shorten the life of the disposal field.

Chemicals not normally used in homes may cause trouble, so it is unwise to risk their disposal in a septic-tank system. These include chemicals used for photography or other hobbies and workshop activities. Substances not likely to decompose easily in a septic tank (toilet-paper substitutes, paper towels, newspapers, rags, etc.) should be disposed of elsewhere. Another thing to avoid is the introduction of large volumes of water, such as the drainage from roofs.

Where an excess of oil, fat and grease is anticipated, it is best to provide a grease trap. The grease is skimmed off the surface frequently so that only clear fluid will pass into the septic tank. With such an installation the discharge of a garbage grinder must not be passed into the grease trap but directly to the septic tank.

Many products, some containing enzymes, are being sold for the purpose of improving operation of septic tanks and to prevent or cure troubles. As far as is known, none of these products has proved of value in properly controlled tests, according to the Department of Health and Human Services. Drain and septic-tank cleaners containing sodium hydroxide or potassium hydroxide should not be used too frequently nor in excessive amounts. (The above findings do not apply to chemicals designed to maintain soil porosity in disposal fields.)

The predominant reasons for trouble in septic-tank disposal systems are: (1) Lack of consideration for the percolation rate of the soil when installing a system; (2) level of ground water

TABLE D ALLOWABLE SLUDGE ACCUMULATION			
LIQUID CAPACITY OF TANK (GALLONS)	LIQUID DEPTH (FEET)		
	3	4	5
	DISTANCE FROM BOTTOM OF OUTLET TO TOP OF SLUDGE (INCHES)		
500	11	16	21
600	8	13	18
750	6	10	13
900	4	7	10
1,000	4	6	8

too high; (3) overloading the system with substances and chemicals that interfere with fermentation or reduce the absorptive quality of the soil in the disposal field; (4) failure to empty a septic tank when necessary, which allows solids to pass into the disposal field and clog it. When soil porosity of the disposal field is reduced for any of the above reasons the effluent can rise to the ground surface which causes an offensive odor and is a definite health hazard.

Flushing disposal lines with water sometimes gives temporary relief, but may not help at all. To remedy the condition in a disposal field of adequate size, and one that originally had sufficient percolation rate, the soil porosity must be restored or a new disposal field provided.

Inspection and cleaning: Although constant fermentation decomposes much of the scum and sludge in a septic tank, inert solids gradually accumulate to the point where the tank must be emptied. This varies considerably according to load. Some tanks will require cleaning within three years. Others may not require cleaning for much longer periods. To be sure that solids in the tank will not pass into the disposal field and clog it, an annual inspection is recommended. This can be done by a septic-tank cleaning concern. For homeowners who prefer doing this themselves, much unnecessary work can be avoided by providing an inspection outlet on the cover slab over the tank outlet. After uncovering this, allow gas in the tank to disperse by ventilation before inspection.

Avoid breathing the gas or igniting a match near it since the gas is both asphyxiating and explosive. Use a stick with a hinged flap to force it through the scum layer near the outlet. Let the flap drop to a horizontal position and then pull the stick up until you feel resistance of the scum layer. Then mark the stick at the top of the inspection outlet. Next, lower it again and pull it up against the lower end of the outlet elbow, tee or baffle, again marking the stick. The difference between the marks is the distance of scum to the outlet.

To measure the sludge thickness, wrap the end of a stick with rough, white toweling and tack it in place. Insert this through the hole previously made in the scum, and push the stick to the tank bottom, turning it as you would an auger. After a few minutes pull it up slowly so some sludge will remain on the toweling and so indicate the sludge thickness.

The tank should be emptied when the lower surface of the scum is about 3 in. above the bottom of the outlet, and as soon as the sludge comes within the limits given in Table D. Usually, tank cleaning is done by means of a tank truck equipped with a pump. An emptied tank should not be washed or disinfected; some of the sludge should be left to resume fermentation.

WITH TWO STICKS you can measure accumulation of sludge to see if tank needs cleaning

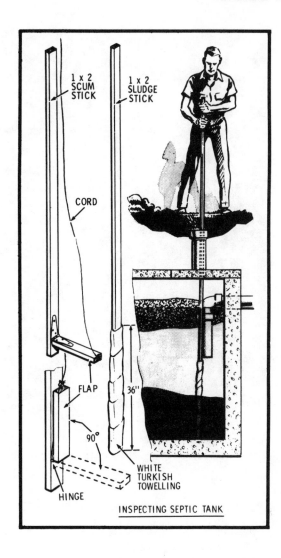

HIGHLY DECORATIVE plywood paneling for study or office is called "brushed reverse board and batten."

Plywood

■ PLYWOOD IS USUALLY THOUGHT OF as a single board measuring up to 4 feet wide and 8 feet long with a thickness from ¼ to ¾ in. Some building material retailers furnish it in smaller sizes and lesser thicknesses, in panels from 1 foot in width up, and in thicknesses down to ⅛ in. These panels are usually called "pre-cuts" and have A-C faces and backs (more later).

Actually, plywood is a series of thinly-cut wood veneers that have been crosslaminated with alternating grain patterns under extreme pressure to provide a dimensionally-stable and water-resistant panel board. Panel fabrication is almost always the same regardless of the top veneers used.

Plywood is available faced with some of the finest cabinet woods, both domestic and exotic, from ash to zebrawood. Some of the finer hardwood facings (top veneers) are very expensive. Plywoods with softwood facings are relatively inexpensive. With such a broad range plywood may be used to build houses, boats, cabinets, furniture, fences, toys.

In the marketplace, plywood is plentiful in two basic types, the one with *hardwood* facings of a wide variety, the other in a variety of *softwood* facings. The latter are most widely used in common applications, largely because of versatility and lower cost per square foot. Both types have back veneers of lesser, but quality, facings, since the backs of the panels seldom show. If both sides will show, panels may be purchased with similar veneers on both facings.

Plywood is sold almost anywhere lumber and other building materials are sold. If you can't find the panels you want, check cabinet and millwork specialty shops and local plywood distributors. These outlets may be found in the advertising pages of the telephone directory.

Hardwood-faced plywoods

Hardwood-faced plywoods are graded somewhat differently than softwood-faced panels. The best grade is *custom* grade (No. 1), free of the patches, knots and plugs that are permissible in the lower grades. It's suitable for the finest work where the wood must be exposed.

Next comes *good* grade (No. 2) with clean, smoothly cut facing and the joints precisely matched so the grain runs true.

The *sound* grade, commonly No. 3, has no open, visible defects but the grain may not be as closely matched and minor mineral streaks and stains are permissible.

In the *utility* grade (No. 4) somewhat greater defects and discolorations are more or less general and in the final, or *reject* grade (No. 5) knot holes and splits are permissible in manufacture. The latter two or three grades are suitable only for rough work where sectional strength and not appearance is the desirable feature.

Hardwood-faced plywoods also come to you in three types of bonds (adhesives) classified as faced with a series of laminated veneers. This plywood is widely used in furniture construction and built-ins. *Particleboard* core is actually a board made up of resin-coated wood particles to a given width and then faced on both sides with laminated veneers in the same manner as lumber core.

All these panels are lightweight, easily workable with hand or power tools and are exceptionally stable.

Softwood plywoods

Many plywoods used for medium and light construction and do-it-yourself projects, are commonly termed "softwood plywoods." These panels are generally classified as to strength and type of glue bond. The face veneers are available in a variety of wood species such as Douglas fir, western larch, and the southern loblolly and longleaf pines. The top facing or veneer may be smooth or finished with any number of different textures and grooves. Strength of the panels is ranked into groups from 1 through 5. Group 1, for example, is the strongest panel; Group 5 is the weakest panel. Group 1 has 10 wood species including beech, birch, fir, and pine—all strong woods. Group 5 has 3 species—basswood, poplar, and balsam—considered "weak" woods. In all, there are some 83 species of woods classified in the five groups. Therefore, when you select a plywood panel, look to the group number for the strength you want. If you are paneling a room, Group 2 is plenty strong enough. If you are installing underlayment Group 1 is required. Panels in Group 1 sometimes are priced higher than those in Groups 2 through 5 for obvious reasons: strength, durability.

Two types of adhesives are used to laminate the wood veneers: exterior and interior, or only exterior. (Interior/intermediate glue sometimes is used, but this type of bond is not commonly available.) Panels designated as "exterior" or EXT are recommended for use where permanent exposure to weather or moisture will be involved. These panels have an exterior glue bond.

Panels designated as "INT" or "interior" or "Exposure 1" are recommended for use where the panels will be subjected to temporary exposure to weather or moisture. Typical would be roof and wall sheathing, interior paneling, cabinets, furniture, shelving. Panels marked with "Exposure 2" usually have an interior/exterior glue bond and may be used in the same applications as those marked "Exposure 1."

Cores for softwood plywoods

Panels are available with a variety of cores or base material to which the facings (top and back) are bonded. *Veneer* cores probably are the most common. They consist of a series of laminated veneers, the laminations alternating at right angles. *Composite* cores are manufactured by gluing reconstituted wood cores—instead of veneers—between the top and back facings of the panels. Composites for all practical purposes look and act similar to all-veneer plywood. Composites are specified for many building projects and are interchangeable with all-veneer plywood panels.

Nonveneered panels are made from structural wood generically classified as waferboard, oriented strand board (OSB), and some classes of structural particleboard. Oversimplified, waferboard is large wafer-like wood flakes that are bonded together with a resin adhesive. OSB is fabricated from cross-laminated and compressed layers of resin-bonded wood strands. Particleboard is made up of wood particles that are bonded at random with a resin adhesive.

All panels are lightweight, with the exception of particleboard. They all may be worked with hand or power tools and are exceptionally stable, free of the tendency of solid-stock construction to warp or "wind." For special projects, plywood is available on special order with fiberglass-reinforced plastic (FRP) and metal overlays bonded to the panel faces. Plywood also can be purchased fire-retardant-treated (FRT) and pressure-preservative-treated.

APA rated trademarks

Plywood, composite, and nonveneered panels manufactured by mills subscribing to the American Plywood Association (APA) are produced in strict accordance with government standards. These standards are so noted on the edge and back stamps on APA panels as PS 1-74, the government standard that applies to this product. All APA performance-rated panels are recognized by the member model building code organizations of the National Research Board (NRB), the International Building Officials and Code Administrators (BOCA) and the Uniform Building Code (UBC), and the Southern Building Code Congress International (SBCCI), promulgators of the Standard Building Code (SBC). You may find some of the panels stamped with these letters, which indicates various code approvals. Another marking may be FHA, UM-66. This stands for Federal Housing Administration Use of Materials Bulletin Number 66. As a rule of thumb, all APA performance-rated panels, regardless of composition or configuration, may be used for structural projects if they are rated with the PS 1-74 stamp. Most building codes will accept this rating.

The trademarks contain a wealth of information. The large, square trademarks are stamped on the back facings of the panels. The long, narrow trademarks are stamped on the edges of the panels. This is done so the veneer is not damaged by the ink used in the stamping process. Here's how to read a typical stamp:

The APA stands for American Plywood Association and means that the mill that manufactured that specific panel is a member of APA. The A-C letters denote the grade of veneer. The A or "good face" is smooth and paintable. The C or "back face" has tight knots and a solid surface. Group 1 means that the panel is fabricated from the strongest wood species. Exterior means that the panel has an exterior glue bond and may be used where permanent exposure to weather or

moisture will be involved. The 000 numbers will be real numbers indicating the mill location where the panel was made. The PS 1-74 mark indicates that the panel meets the government requirement for this plywood specification.

Sheathing stamps are somewhat different. For example: the APA stands for American Plywood Association. Rated Sheathing means the panel has been rated by APA for sheathing according to the specification set down by the National Research Board (NRB-108). The numbers 42/20 (they may be different) mean that the sheathing may be used over rafters that are spaced no more than 42 in. on center, or over joists that are no more than 20 in. on center. The first number always applies to rafters; the second to joists or studs. The ⅝ figure means the sheathing is ⅝-in. thick. Sized for spacing indicates that the panel is slightly undersized so the joints between adjoining panels may be spaced ⅛ in. to allow for expansion/contraction of the panel. Exterior indicates an exterior glue bond; 000 is the mill number.

Still another stamp is the APA Rated Sturdi-I-Floor. This is a touch-sanded panel designed for residential, light-frame single-floor installations. It serves as both structural subflooring and an underlayment for finish flooring. The panels have span ratings of 16, 20, 24, and 48 in. on center, and this is so marked on the grade stamp. The panels are sized for spacing (⅛-in.), and tongue-and-grooved, noted by the inscription "T&G Net Width 47½ (in.)" with a 1 Exposure (glue bond as noted above).

Softwood grades

The top and back facings or veneers of the panels are graded for appearance as well as strength. The inner plies of exterior plywood do not permit "D" graded veneers for strength reasons. Interior plywood permits A, B, C, and D graded veneers in its manufacture since strength is not as important.

The top and back facings are graded as N, A, B, C, C-plugged, and D. The facings can be any combination of these letters (grades).

N-grade is a special order "natural finish" veneer. It is select all heartwood or all sapwood. It is free of open defects, but allows some repairs. N-grade usually isn't stocked by building material retailers mainly because of its high cost. If your project calls for N-grade panels, expect to wait from four to six weeks for special-order delivery.

A-grade is smooth and paintable. Neatly made repairs in the veneer are permissible. The panels

SOME COMMON GRADES OF PLYWOOD

Grade Designation	Description & Common Uses	Typical Trademarks	Veneer Grade Face	Inner Plies	Back	1/4	5/16	3/8	1/2	5/8	3/4
APA N-N, N-A, N-B INT	Cabinet quality. For natural finish furniture, cabinet doors, built-ins, etc. Special order items. (2)	N-N • G-1 • INT-APA • PS1-74 • 000	N	C	N,A or B						●
APA N-D INT	For natural finish paneling. Special order item. (2)	N-D • G-2 • INT-APA • PS1-74 • 000	N	D	D	●					
APA A-A INT	For applications with both sides on view: built-ins, cabinets, furniture, partitions. Smooth face, suitable for painting. (2)	A-A • G-1 • INT-APA • PS1-74 • 000	A	D	A	●		●	●	●	●
APA A-B INT	Use where appearance of one side is less important but where two solid surfaces are necessary. (2)	A-B • G-1 • INT-APA • PS1-74 • 000	A	D	B	●		●	●	●	●
APA A-D INT	Use where appearance of only one side is important: paneling, built-ins, shelving, partitions, flow racks. (2)	APA A-D GROUP 1 INTERIOR 000 PS 1-74 EXTERIOR GLUE	A	D	D	●		●	●	●	●
APA B-B INT	Utility panel with two solid sides. Permits circular plugs. (2)	B-B • G-2 • INT-APA • PS1-74 • 000	B	D	B	●		●	●	●	●
APA B-D INT	Utility panel with one solid side. Good for backing, sides of built-ins, industry shelving, slip sheets, separator boards, bins. (2)	APA B-D GROUP 2 INTERIOR 000 PS 1-74 EXTERIOR GLUE	B	D	D	●		●	●	●	●
APA UNDERLAYMENT INT	For application over structural subfloor. Provides smooth surface for application of resilient floor coverings. Touch-sanded. Also available with exterior glue. (3)	APA UNDERLAYMENT GROUP 1 INTERIOR 000 PS 1-74 EXTERIOR GLUE	C Plgd.	C & D	D			●	●	● 19/32	● 23/32
APA C-D PLUGGED INT	For built-ins, wall and ceiling tile backing, cable reels, walkways, separator boards. Not a substitute for UNDERLAYMENT or STURD-I-FLOOR as it lacks their indentation resistance. Touch-sanded. Also made with exterior glue. (3)	APA C-D PLUGGED GROUP 1 INTERIOR 000 PS 1-74 EXTERIOR GLUE	C Plgd.	D	D				●	● 19/32	● 23/32
APA DECORATIVE INT	Rough-sawn, brushed, grooved, or striated faces. For paneling, interior accent walls, built-ins, counter facing, display exhibits. (5)	APA DECORATIVE GROUP 2 INTERIOR 000 PS 1-74	C or btr.	D	D		●	●	●	●	
APA PLYRON INT	Hardboard face on both sides. For countertops shelving, cabinet doors, flooring. Faces tempered, untempered, smooth or screened.	PLYRON-INT-APA • 000	C & D					●		●	●

	Grade Designation	Description & Common Uses	Typical Trademarks	Common Thicknesses (in.)				
				5/16	3/8	1/2	5/8	3/4
PROTECTED OR INTERIOR USE	APA RATED SHEATHING EXP 1 or 2	Specially designed for subflooring and wall and roof sheathing, but can also be used for a broad range of other construction and industrial applications. Can be manufactured as conventional veneered plywood, as composite, or as a nonveneered panel. For special engineered applications, including high load requirements and certain industrial uses, veneered panels conforming to PS 1 may be required. Specify Exposure 1 when long construction delays are anticipated.	APA RATED SHEATHING 32/16 1/2 INCH SIZED FOR SPACING EXPOSURE 2 000 NRB-108	●	●	● 7/16	●	●
	APA STRUCTURAL I & II RATED SHEATHING EXP 1	Unsanded all-veneer PS 1 plywood grades for use where strength properties are of maximum importance: structural diaphragms, box beams, gusset plates, stressed-skin panels, containers, pallet bins. Made only with exterior glue (Exposure 1). STRUCTURAL I more commonly available. (3)	APA RATED SHEATHING 24 oc 3/8 INCH SIZED FOR SPACING EXPOSURE 1 000 PS 1-74 C-C INT/EXT GLUE NRB-108	●	●	●	●	●
	APA RATED STURD-I-FLOOR EXP 1 or 2	For combination subfloor-underlayment. Provides smooth surface for application of resilient floor covering and possesses high concentrated and impact load resistance. Can be manufactured as conventional veneered plywood, as a composite, or as a nonveneered panel. Available square edge or tongue-and-groove. Specify Exposure 1 when long construction delays are anticipated.	APA RATED STURD-I-FLOOR 24 oc 23/32 INCH SIZED FOR SPACING T&G NET WIDTH 47-1/2 EXPOSURE 1 000 NRB-108				● 19/32	● 23/32
	APA RATED STURD-I-FLOOR 48 oc (2-4-1) EXP 1	For combination subfloor-underlayment on 32- and 48-inch spans and for heavy timber roof construction. Provides smooth surface for application of resilient floor coverings and possesses high concentrated and impact load resistance. Manufactured only as conventional veneered plywood and only with exterior glue (Exposure 1). Available square edge or tongue-and-groove.	APA RATED STURD-I-FLOOR 48oc (2-4-1) 1-1/8 INCH SIZED FOR SPACING EXPOSURE 1 T&G 000 INT/EXT GLUE NRB-108 FHA-UM-66			1-1/8		
EXTERIOR USE	APA RATED SHEATHING EXT	Exterior sheathing panel for subflooring and wall and roof sheathing, siding on service and farm buildings, crating, pallets, pallet bins, cable reels, etc. Manufactured as conventional veneered plywood.	APA RATED SHEATHING 48/24 3/4 INCH SIZED FOR SPACING EXTERIOR 000 NRB-108	●	●	●	●	●
	APA STRUCTURAL I & II RATED SHEATHING EXT	For engineered applications in construction and industry where resistance to permanent exposure to weather or moisture is required. Manufactured only as conventional veneered PS 1 plywood. Unsanded. STRUCTURAL I more commonly available. (3)	APA RATED SHEATHING STRUCTURAL I 24/0 3/8 INCH SIZED FOR SPACING EXTERIOR 000 PS 1-74 C-C NRB-108	●	●	●	●	●
	APA RATED STURD-I-FLOOR EXT	For combination subfloor-underlayment under resilient floor coverings where severe moisture conditions may be present, as in balcony decks. Possesses high concentrated and impact load resistance. Manufactured as conventional veneered plywood. Available square edge or tongue-and-groove.	APA RATED STURD-I-FLOOR 20 oc 19/32 INCH SIZED FOR SPACING T&G NET WIDTH 47-1/2 EXTERIOR 000 NRB-108				● 19/32	● 23/32

Table title: **SOME CONSTRUCTION PLYWOODS**

may be used for a natural finish in less demanding applications.

B-grade has a solid surface veneer. Circular repair plugs and tight knots are permitted.

C-grade has knotholes up to 1 in. Occasional knotholes ½ in. larger are permitted providing the total width of all knots and knotholes within a specified section doesn't exceed certain limits. Limited splits are permitted; minimum veneer.

C-plugged has improved C-veneer with splits limited to ⅛ in. in width and knotholes and borer holes limited to ¼x½ in.

D-grade permits knots and knotholes to 2½ in. in width and ½ in. larger under certain specified limits. Limited splits are permitted.

"Repaired" plywood panels are just as strong as those without repairs. However, the patches are sometimes made with a synthetic material that does not absorb stain finish as evenly as the wood surrounding the patch. Therefore, if you finish with stain, use a heavy-bodied stain (not transparent) so the patches will be hidden.

Interior grade use-guide

What grade and type of plywood you buy depends, of course, on the project at hand. Below is a guide to interior appearance grades:

A-A INT-APA: Both faces are the highest standard veneer grade for use where both sides will show: built-ins, cabinets, furniture, partitions, etc. The most common thicknesses are: ¼ in., ⅜ in., ½ in., ⅝ in., ¾ in. and 1 in. The veneer grade is A face, A back and D-grade inner.

A-B INT-APA: This panel is similar to A-A, but it is used where the appearance of one side is less important, and two smooth solid surfaces are desirable. Thicknesses are the same.

A-D INT-APA: Used for built-ins, paneling, shelving, partitions, etc., where only one side will show. Thicknesses are standard, with D inner plys.

B-B INT-APA: An interior utility panel for use as partitions, utility built-ins, mounting boards, etc. Both sides are smooth and may be painted. Thicknesses are standard, with D inner plys.

B-D INT-APA: For use where one smooth side is needed. Shelving, sides and backs for built-ins, economy cabinet work, slip sheets, separator boards and bins. Standard thickness; inner plys, D.

DECORATIVE PANELS: This material is rough sawn, brushed, grooved, striated or embossed on one side. Use it for accent walls, paneling, counter fronts and where wood with various surface textures is desired. The most common thicknesses are ⁵⁄₁₆ in., ⅜ in., and ½ in. Veneer grade is C or better face, plys, D back and D inner.

PLYRON: These panels have a hardboard face and back and are used for built-ins, cabinet doors, countertops, worktables and furniture. The faces may be tempered, untempered, smooth or screened hardboard. The most common thicknesses are ½ in., ⅝ in. and ¾ in., with C and D inner plys.

N-N INT-APA: A natural finish cabinet-quality panel, designed to be used where both sides will show. Both sides are select all heartwood or all sapwood veneer. Typical uses are for cabinet doors, built-ins and furniture having a natural finish. The panels are usually a special order item. In thicknesses of ¾ in. only with C inner plys.

N-A and N-B INT-APA: This is similar to the grade listed above, but it permits an A or B-grade veneer on the backside. The panel is designed for economy when building cabinet doors, built-ins, furniture. It is a special-order item in ¾-in. thickness only with C inner plys.

N-D INT-APA: One side is select all heartwood or all sapwood veneer. Use it for interior paneling that will have a natural finish. Usually a special order item in ¼-in. thickness only with D inner plys.

UNDERLAYMENT INT-APA: For underlayment or combination subfloor-underlayment under resilient floor coverings. Ply beneath the face is C or D veneer; it is sanded or touch sanded as specified. Most common thicknesses: ¼, ⅜, ½, ⅝ and ¾ in.

A-A EXT-APA: Designed for exposed applications where both sides will show: fences, windscreens, exterior cabinets and built-ins, boats, etc. The most common thicknesses are: ¼, ⅜, ½, ⅝, ¾ and 1 in. Panels have an A face and back with C inner plys.

A-B EXT-APA: Similar uses to A-A EXT, but where the appearance of one side is less important. The thicknesses are the same with C inner plys.

MDO EXT-APA: A medium-density overlaid plywood panel with opaque resin-impregnated fiber overlay, heat-fused to one or both panel faces. It provides an ideal base for paint. Uses including siding, soffits, windscreens, exterior painted cabinet work, etc. Thicknesses: ⁵⁄₁₆, ⅜, ½, ⅝, ¾ and 1 in. Veneer grade is B face, B or C back, C or C-plugged inner plys.

TEXTURE 1-11: The unsanded panels have parallel grooves ¼ in. deep, ⅜ in. wide on 2-in. or 4-in. centers. The edges are shiplapped for a continuous visual pattern. Uses include siding, accent paneling, fences, etc. It is available in 8 and 10-ft. lengths and sanded or with MD overlay. Thicknesses: ⅝ in. only; C or better face, C back and inner plys.

303 SPECIALTY SIDING EXT-APA: The grade covers proprietary plywood products for siding, fencing, soffits, windscreens and other exterior applications or interior panels. The panels have special surface treatments which include rough-sawn, striated and brushed, and may be V-grooved, etc. It is available in redwood, cedar, hemlock, Douglas fir, lauan and other woods. The most common thicknesses are ⅜, ½ and ⅝ in. The veneer grade is B or better face, C back and plys.

PLYRON EXT-APA: The panels are surfaced on both sides with tempered hardboard with smooth or screened surfaces. Thicknesses are ½,

IN PANELING A WALL, furring strips are applied to fit panels, then adhesive is applied to strips.

PANELING IS APPLIED over the furring strips. Be sure the edge of the first panel is vertical.

⅝, and ¾ in. The panels have C inner plys.

MARINE EXT-APA: Marine-grade panels are made only with Douglas fir or western larch, and a special solid joined core construction. The panels are subject to special limitations on core gaps and the number of face repairs. Use them for boat hulls.

C-C PLUGGED EXT-APA: For exterior underlayment, these panels are also ideal for tile backing where a permanently waterproof material is needed. The panels are sanded or touch sanded as specified. The most common thicknesses are ¼, ⅜, ½, ⅝, ¾ and ⅞ in. The veneer grade is C (plugged) face, D back and inner plys.

The types and grades mentioned above are generally available in 4x8-ft. panels. However, other lengths and widths are manufactured. The larger sizes can be ordered by a building material retailer. You can expect a 4 to 6 week delivery delay, and, if small quantities are ordered, you may be expected to pay for freight costs.

Shopping tips

Many building material retailers have "plywood bins" in which random-size pieces and trimmings are available. Some dealers also will cut panels for you in different sizes. You have to buy the entire panel, however, before your specific cuts are made. Many retailers also stock "pre-cuts" or "ready-cuts." These are priced a bit higher than panels that you would cut yourself. The face veneers of pre-cuts usually are A and C; edge voids are filled.

Before buying plywood, it is often to your advantage to preplan the project at hand so the amount of material required may be purchased at one time. Costs sometimes can be cut with quantity if you ask the retailer for this discount. Any irregular sizes may be picked out of the plywood bins and pre-cuts—another cost savings.

Most important, in structural projects such as roof sheathing, underlayment, and siding, be sure that the panels conform to local building codes. Group 1 and span-rated panels usually are accepted by all code groups. On some grade stamps on siding you may note these numbers and letters: "18-S/W." This means that there are 18 synthetic and/or wooden patches permitted in the panel. The number can go as low as 6-S/W. This is important when buying the siding if the siding will be stained. The fewer the patches, the less "show-through" of patches through the stain, which should be heavy-bodied instead of clear or semi-transparent.

Working with plywood

Plywood panels are easy to work with, although there are several tips that will make the job even easier:

HERE'S A TEXTURED exterior paneling that is easy to apply. Seal the edges of exterior panels.

MANY PLYWOOD PANELS designed for covering walls are available prefinished.

1. To prevent waste, lay out the panel for cutting. If there will be many pieces cut from a single panel, sketch the arrangement on a piece of paper before you transfer it to the panel as a cutting pattern. Allow for the saw kerf between the pieces. Have the grain of the panel running the long way of the piece, if possible.

2. If you use a handsaw, cut the panel with the best face up. Use a saw with 10 to 15 points to the inch and support the panel on sawhorses so it won't sag. Always use a sharp saw.

3. For power sawing on a table saw, cut with the good face of the panel up. Use a sharp combination blade or fine-tooth blade without too much set. The blade should be set so it protrudes above the panel about the height of the teeth.

4. With a portable power saw, place the good face of the panel down.

5. When planing edges, work from both ends of the edge toward the center of the panel. This will prevent splitting out the plys at the end of the cut. Always use a plane with a sharp blade and set it to take a fine shaving. Work slowly.

6. Since plywood is sanded smooth at the time it is made, sanding it before a sealer or prime coat of finish should be confined to the edges. After the surface is sealed, however, you may sand in the direction of the grain only.

7. It is difficult to nail or screw into the edges of veneer-core plywood. Plan your work so you can avoid these problems.

Plywood panels can be bent to certain minimum radii depending, of course, on the thickness of the panel. In some applications you may have to bend two thin panels to build up a particular thickness. For example, ¾-in. panels can be bent only in a circle with a 10-ft. radius, while ⅜-in. panels can be bent to a radius of 36 in. Two layers of the ⅜-in. material will produce a much sharper bend and yet will give you the same effect as a ¾-in. panel.

Plywood panels are ideal for concrete forming. If the panels will be used for more than one project, the face that will be next to the concrete should be coated with form oil, which is brushed on. If you will be doing lots of concrete work where plywood forms are necessary, it is recommended that you buy APA B-B Plyform Class I or Class II panels that have a very high reuse factor. These panels are sanded both sides and are mill-oiled unless otherwise specified. The Class I panels are the strongest.

Hide plywood edges 16 ways

■ PLYWOOD HAS long presented the home workman with the problem of hiding the material's laminated edges from view. The simplest do-it-yourself technique has been to cover them with paper-thin wood tape. It's sold in rolls in a choice of woods and merely glued on. This is okay for book shelves and perhaps the square edges of a tabletop, but it's not too durable a solution if the project will get lots of handling and wear. And wood tape, limited to plain square edges, is no help when you want shaped edges on a piece of furniture. But here are many ways to hide the laminations and add eye appeal at the same time. They range from comparatively simple to more involved approaches.

For the ultimate in hiding nails, a small gouge is often used to lift a chip of wood first. The nail or brad is then driven and the chip is glued back in place over the head. On fairly small projects, rubber bands cut from a large inner tube are handy for clamping molding to the plywood edge.

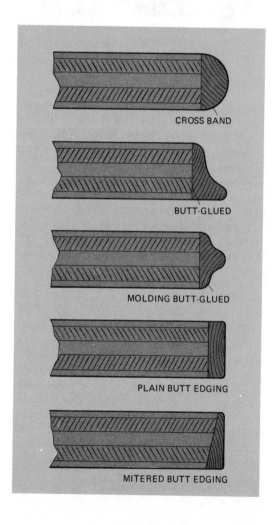

CROSS BAND

BUTT-GLUED

MOLDING BUTT-GLUED

PLAIN BUTT EDGING

MITERED BUTT EDGING

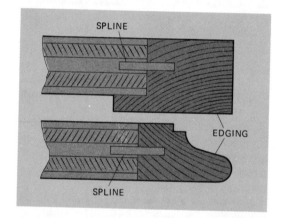

SPLINE

EDGING

SPLINE

Simple butt-gluing moldings to straight plywood edges can dress them up. Five approaches are shown at left. Small finishing nails or brads are added, their heads set and puttied over. For the ultimate in hiding nails, a small gouge is often used to lift a chip of wood first. The nail or brad is then driven and the chip is glued back in place over the head. On fairly small projects, rubber bands cut from a large inner tube are handy for clamping molding to the plywood edge.

Splines form exceptionally strong joints. They're popular where there is room for them, as with wider moldings. With a table saw, run kerfs in both the molding and plywood and rip thin wood splines to fit the kerfs. A rabbet in the molding, plus the spline and glue, makes a joint so strong that the edge stiffens the plywood.

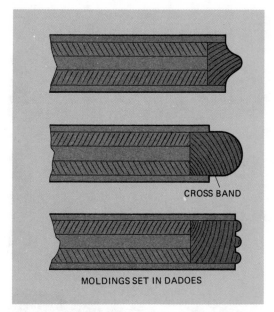

MOLDINGS SET IN DADOES

CROSS BAND

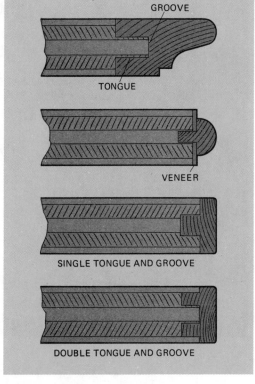

GROOVE

TONGUE

VENEER

SINGLE TONGUE AND GROOVE

DOUBLE TONGUE AND GROOVE

Insetting moldings in dadoes turns the plywood veneer plies into a part of the decorative edge. A dado in the core laminations gets a depth to suit the molding. That top depth brings the veneer ply flush with the molding, but the outer veneers can also make decorative shoulders. Pinch clamps will hold surface veneers against the molding while glue sets.

Tongue-and-groove joints are far less likely to pull loose. Grooves can be cut in the plywood, or in the molding. The second drawing shows how an edge treatment can be built up, with narrow molding added to a veneer strip.

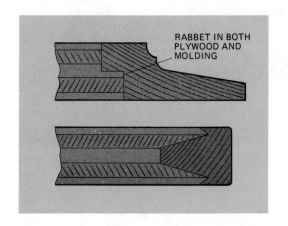

RABBET IN BOTH PLYWOOD AND MOLDING

In special approaches, you see how fancy, wide picture-frame molding can be the edging. It is perhaps the strongest joint of all—but one that takes special cutters to form both the plywood groove and the molding. After such a start, you might end up by shaping the exposed face of the molding itself.

Plywood cutoff jig you can build

■ IF YOU NEED to cut up a full sheet of plywood only once in a while, you aren't going to bother making this cutoff jig. You'll first saw it roughly to a size that's fairly easy to handle and take it from there, not caring particularly if you waste some material in doing so.

However, if you run a small cabinet shop where you are working daily with these big, awkward sheets, it will pay you to make this handy labor-saver.

It consists of a 60x96-in. base on which the plywood sheet is placed, and a saw guide which is hinged to swing down on top of the work. A built-in track and kerf in the guide, which is made to fit your particular portable electric saw, lets

JIG STORES AGAINST WALL when not in use. Note latch-fitted handle to raise and lower jig.

you zip across the sheet in nothing flat, resulting in a perfect 90° cut.

When not in use, the jig is swung up against the wall, clearing the benchtop for other use. You can either attach the jig directly to the wall or bolt it to the rear edge of the bench on which it's used. A 1x2 handle hinged under the front of the jig is fitted with a spring-loaded bolt latch and

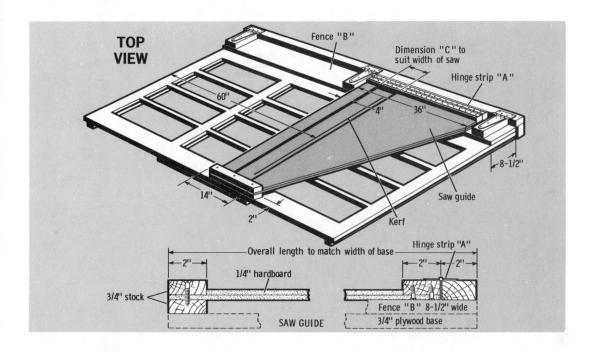

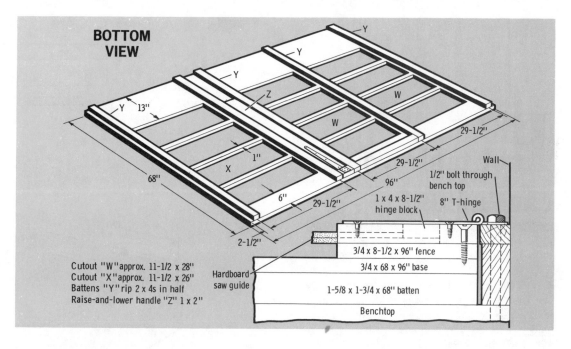

chain to make it handy to swing the jig up against the wall and lock it securely in place. As an extra precaution, a king-size turnbutton will give added assurance that it won't come crashing down accidentally.

The details clearly show how it's made. The base is a 4x8-ft. sheet with a 20-in. piece splined to it to make it 68 in. wide, then cut as shown to make it lighter and self-clearing of sawdust. It's important in hinging the hardboard saw guide to be sure that it is exactly 90° to fence "B."

The jig will accommodate both plywood and lumber up to ¾ in. thick. Thinner stock is cut by shimming it up with scrap pieces. The track for the saw is made just wide enough to let it slide smoothly, yet without any side play.

Pool table you can build

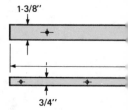

■ IF YOU HAVE DONE any shopping lately you know that a pool table is an expensive item to buy. However, if you are good at working with tools you can save by building this beauty yourself. Such hard-to-get items as billiard cloth, cushion rubber and foam padding come in a kit.

This table is well-designed and if constructed with care, it can prove to be very strong and durable. It features a sturdy pedestal base, plastic-laminated aprons, drop pockets which simplify the construction, and padded rails—an extra usually found only on more expensive tables.

The table is standard size (3½ x 7 ft.) and uses 2¼-in. balls.

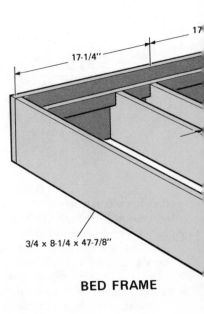

3/4 x 8-1/4 x 47-7/8''

BED FRAME

1-1/2''
FH SC

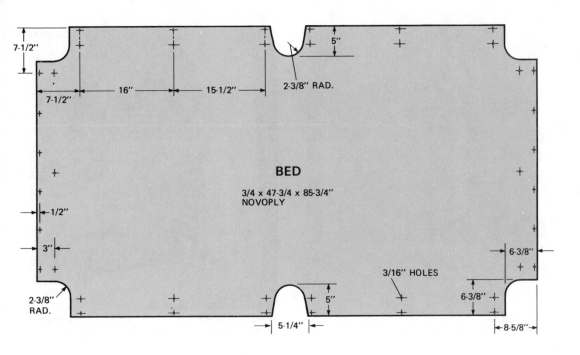

7-1/2″

7-1/2″

16″ 15-1/2″

5″

2-3/8″ RAD.

BED

3/4 x 47-3/4 x 85-3/4″
NOVOPLY

1/2″

3″

6-3/8″

3/16″ HOLES

2-3/8″
RAD.

6-3/8″

5″

5-1/4″

8-5/8″

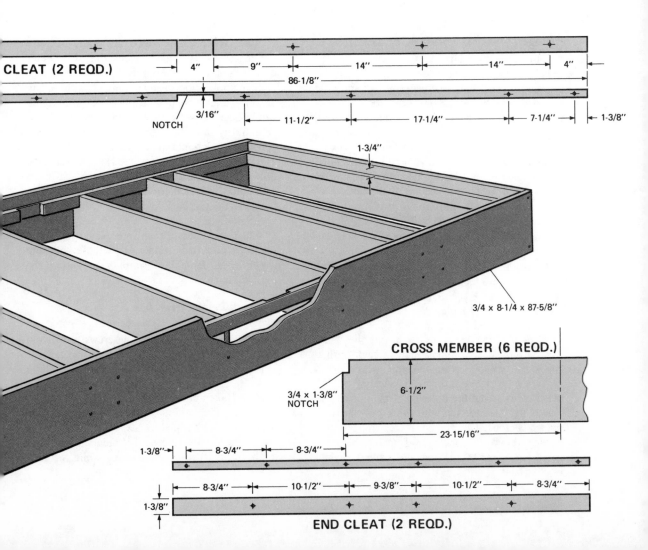

CLEAT (2 REQD.)

4″ 9″ 14″ 14″ 4″

86-1/8″

NOTCH

3/16″

11-1/2″ 17-1/4″ 7-1/4″ 1-3/8″

1-3/4″

3/4 x 8-1/4 x 87-5/8″

CROSS MEMBER (6 REQD.)

3/4 x 1-3/8″
NOTCH

6-1/2″

23-15/16″

1-3/8″ 8-3/4″ 8-3/4″

8-3/4″ 10-1/2″ 9-3/8″ 10-1/2″ 8-3/4″

1-3/8″

END CLEAT (2 REQD.)

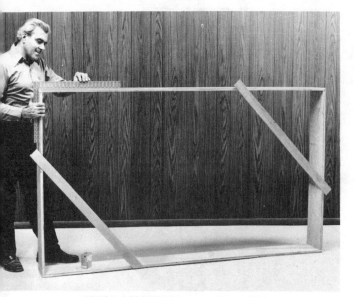

APRON ASSEMBLY is squared up with temporary diagonal braces of scrap across two corners.

SCREWDRIVER BIT in a variable-speed drill makes quick work of driving home the many screws needed.

Materials readily available

● **Base.** All materials used in the table are readily available. Except where noted, ¾-in. plywood is used. Even the pedestal legs and base are made of plywood, using box-type construction which adds much to rigidity and sturdiness. Leg uprights are rabbeted to minimize edge grain, and base sections are butt-joined.

To insure accuracy and to simplify assembly, the uprights should be temporarily mounted to the pedestal *before* the scallop at the bottom of the pedestal is cut. Mount the uprights individually before they are "boxed." You will note in the material list that extra length has been allowed for this reason.

Miter the uprights at 14° from the vertical, top and bottom, then at the center of the pedestal mark two lines $8^{15}/_{16}$ in. apart. Align the uprights on these marks, keeping the bottom even with the bottom edge of the pedestal. Tack the pieces in place with 1¼-in. brads, then drill pilot holes for the screws. Use four screws in each upright for added strength. Once located, you can remove the uprights and cut the scallop in the pedestal and recut the bottoms of the uprights to match the scallop. Uprights now may be permanently glued. The leg filler pieces are rabbeted, leaving ⅛ in. of stock as indicated. These are glued just short of the top and extend slightly into the base.

Note: When gluing edge-grain stock, glue-size the edges. Apply thinned glue (thin with water if white glue) to edges and allow to dry before regular application of glue. This seals the edge, preventing excessive absorption of glue which would cause a weak joint. Remember, this is to be a sturdy table throughout and a good careful construction job makes that possible.

Before installing the base pads to the scallops, drill a ½-in. hole at the center of each and insert a T-nut. These are for the leveling jacks. The flange of the nut must be to the outside when the pad is mounted.

When the pedestals are completed, add two furring strips to the upper ends; these will help support the table and simplify mounting the pedestal later.

Now make the stretcher

The stretcher can be made now and the two pedestals connected to it. Lagscrews are driven from the inside to join the pedestals. Do not use glue as you may need to disassemble the table to move it to its final destination. Lagscrews can easily be taken out for such a move.

● **Apron.** The apron consists of a rectangular frame to which the bed, cleats and cross members are attached with screws. To maintain accuracy of the frame, use diagonal strips while the glue sets.

LAGSCREWS attach table to base. Do not use glue so the table can be dismantled easily for moving.

TEMPORARY JIG nailed between uprights of base assures accuracy during assembly.

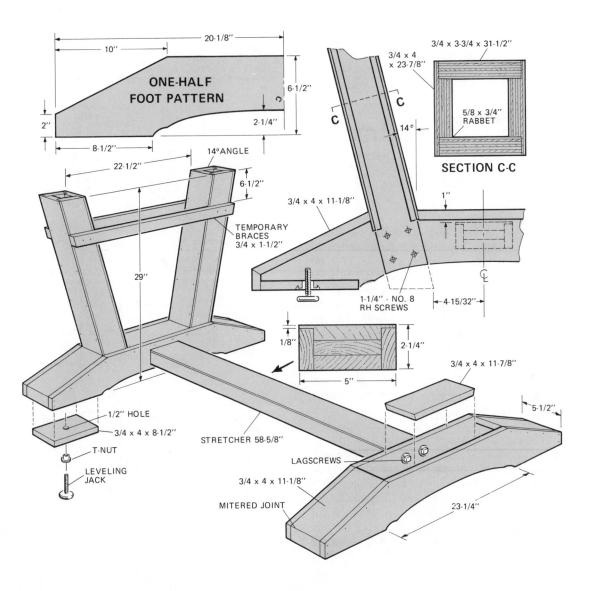

20-1/8''

10''

ONE-HALF
FOOT PATTERN

6-1/2''

2-1/4''

2''

8-1/2''

14° ANGLE

22-1/2''

6-1/2''

TEMPORARY
BRACES
3/4 x 1-1/2''

29''

1/2'' HOLE

3/4 x 4 x 8-1/2''

T-NUT

LEVELING
JACK

STRETCHER 58-5/8''

3/4 x 4 x 11-1/8''

MITERED JOINT

LAGSCREWS

3/4 x 4 x 11-1/8''

3/4 x 4 x 11-7/8''

5-1/2''

23-1/4''

3/4 x 3-3/4 x 31-1/2''

3/4 x 4
x 23-7/8''

14°

5/8 x 3/4''
RABBET

SECTION C-C

C   C

1''

1-1/4'' - NO. 8
RH SCREWS

4-15/32''

1/8''

5''

2-1/4''

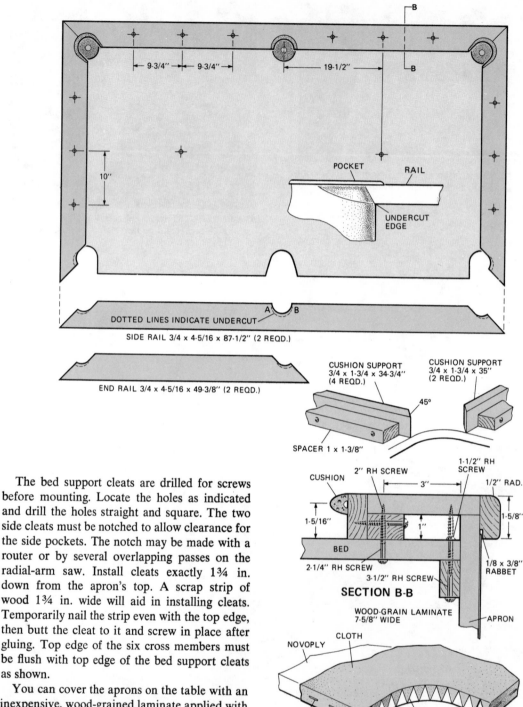

9-3/4″ 9-3/4″ 19-1/2″

10″

POCKET   RAIL

UNDERCUT
EDGE

A   B

DOTTED LINES INDICATE UNDERCUT

SIDE RAIL 3/4 x 4-5/16 x 87-1/2″ (2 REQD.)

END RAIL 3/4 x 4-5/16 x 49-3/8″ (2 REQD.)

CUSHION SUPPORT
3/4 x 1-3/4 x 34-3/4″
(4 REQD.)

CUSHION SUPPORT
3/4 x 1-3/4 x 35″
(2 REQD.)

45°

SPACER 1 x 1-3/8″

CUSHION

2″ RH SCREW

1-1/2″ RH
SCREW

1/2″ RAD.

3″

1-5/16″

1″

1-5/8″

BED

2-1/4″ RH SCREW

3-1/2″ RH SCREW

1/8 x 3/8″
RABBET

SECTION B-B

WOOD-GRAIN LAMINATE
7-5/8″ WIDE

APRON

NOVOPLY

CLOTH

STAPLES

SLITS CUT IN CLOTH
AT POCKETS

The bed support cleats are drilled for screws before mounting. Locate the holes as indicated and drill the holes straight and square. The two side cleats must be notched to allow clearance for the side pockets. The notch may be made with a router or by several overlapping passes on the radial-arm saw. Install cleats exactly 1¾ in. down from the apron's top. A scrap strip of wood 1¾ in. wide will aid in installing cleats. Temporarily nail the strip even with the top edge, then butt the cleat to it and screw in place after gluing. Top edge of the six cross members must be flush with top edge of the bed support cleats as shown.

You can cover the aprons on the table with an inexpensive, wood-grained laminate applied with contact cement. It's offered in rolls 36 in. wide and sold by the foot. It is easy to install and gives the table a nicely finished look. Various colors, patterns and grains are available. It can be cut with scissors, but you may find it easier to score the surface with an awl and snap it along the scored line.

SLIT FABRIC at drop-pocket cutouts and staple it to the underside of the rail, then along rail edges.

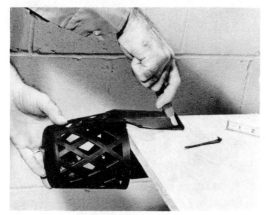

TRIM POCKETS to fit—differently at the sides than at the corners. See the drawing, above right.

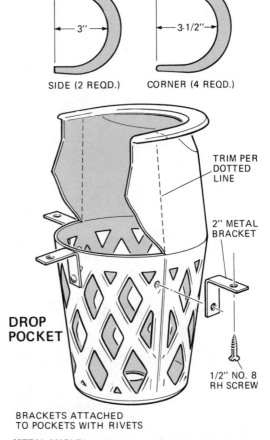

SIDE (2 REQD.)   CORNER (4 REQD.)

3"   3-1/2"

TRIM PER DOTTED LINE

2" METAL BRACKET

DROP POCKET

1/2" NO. 8 RH SCREW

BRACKETS ATTACHED TO POCKETS WITH RIVETS

METAL ANGLE brackets are used to attach drop pockets in cutouts after trimming the pockets.

Cut the laminate slightly oversize and apply contact cement to it and to the wood surface. Allow the cement to dry until it loses its tackiness, then apply carefully. Once in place, it cannot be moved. The top edge of the laminate is set $\frac{11}{16}$ in. below the top edge of the apron. The sides and bottom should overhang slightly. Trim excess with a router fitted with a laminate trimmer or by hand with a plane. Cover the end aprons first, then the longer sides.

● **Bed.** The bed is cut from a sheet of ¾-in. particleboard. Notice that ¼ in. is trimmed from the 48-in. dimension. The length of the bed is 85¾ in. The material is dense and tough, but it is easily cut with ordinary tools such as a portable saw, sabre saw, or even a handsaw. Lay out the corner and side-pocket cutouts according to the diagram. After cutting, break all sharp edges with sandpaper. Drill the mounting holes, then cover with billiard cloth. The cloth is stapled to the underside of the bed. Do the long sides first, then the ends. Slit the cloth at the pockets, stopping the slits just short of the cutouts. Pull the cloth evenly around the pockets and staple to the underside of the bed. (Before installing the cloth remove wrinkles with a steam iron.) The bed and the felt on it are two of the most critical parts of any pool table.

● **Rails.** The rails require some tricky sabre-saw cutting. Cut the sections to size and miter the ends 45°. Place the four pieces on a flat surface and lay out the 4⅛-in.-dia. cutouts.

Make cutouts in the usual manner using a sabre saw. After all corner and sidepocket cutouts have been made, tilt your saw's base to 30° and recut the section of the cutout from points A and B. Undercutting is needed to clear the drop pockets.

The outer edging for the rails is cut and rabbeted as in the drawing. Two passes on the table

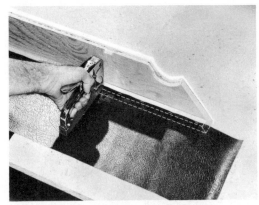

FABRIC-BACKED vinyl is stapled to the underside of rails with $5/16$-in. staples spaced about 1 in. apart.

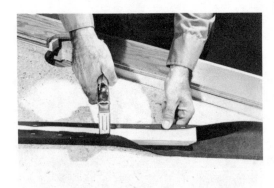

COVER CUSHIONS with 5-in. wide strips of billiard cloth, pulled taut and stapled to the rear side.

CUSHION ENDS are glued as shown, then cloth is pinched and trimmed neatly with a razor blade.

HERE'S HOW a drop pocket fits the corner hole. Front padded rail has been removed for clarity.

saw will form the rabbet—or use a router. Round off top and bottom edges, miter the ends, then nail and glue edge pieces to the four rails.

Padding the rails is not too difficult. Glue a 5-in.-wide strip of foam to the rear edge of the rail just before the round starts. Use rubber cement or Pliobond *only*. Contact cement, white glue and animal glues destroy the foam. If you use rubber cement (sold at stationery and art stores), apply it to both surfaces and let it air-dry about five minutes before joining the parts. Apply a narrow strip of cement about ½ in. wide.

Cover the rails with a strip of fabric-backed vinyl. This is upholstery material; two well-known trade names are Naugahyde and Bolta-flex. Cut it in 9-in.-wide strips and let the ends overhang the rails slightly. Staple one edge of the vinyl to the rabbeted part of the rail back. Pull this taut toward the front of the rail and staple it again on the front edge, with staples about 1 in.

apart. At the cutouts, slit material and staple it to the underside as shown. At the ends of the rails, trim the excess and where impractical to staple, use cement.

When all rails are covered and mounted to the table, there will be a slight gap at the miters. This is rectified by inserting corner fillers made by folding a piece of vinyl over a foam strip. Insert in corners before permanently mounting the rails.
● **Cushions.** The rubber cushions are cemented to the wood cushion supports with rubber or contact cement. The cushion rubber is not symmetrical, but has a top and bottom. It's mounted right when the nose of the rubber is $1^{15}/16$ in. from bottom edge of the support. Miter the supports as indicated, then mount the rubber. Let rubber extend past the miter, then trim it flush with a sharp knife. It's much easier to cut if the blade is dipped in water first.

Covering the cushions is next. Cushion cloth in the kit is 10 in. wide, with a small slit at the

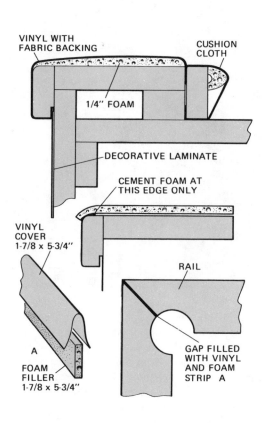

VINYL WITH
FABRIC BACKING

CUSHION
CLOTH

1/4" FOAM

DECORATIVE LAMINATE

CEMENT FOAM AT
THIS EDGE ONLY

VINYL
COVER
1-7/8 x 5-3/4"

RAIL

A
FOAM
FILLER
1-7/8 x 5-3/4"

GAP FILLED
WITH VINYL
AND FOAM
STRIP A

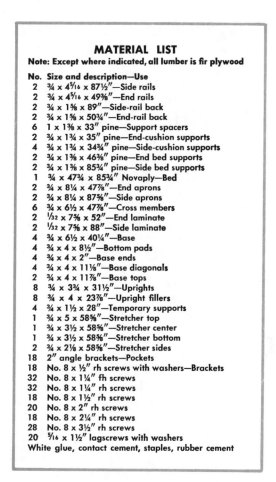

MATERIAL LIST

Note: Except where indicated, all lumber is fir plywood

No.	Size and description—Use
2	¾ x 4⁵⁄₁₆ x 87½"—Side rails
2	¾ x 4⁵⁄₁₆ x 49⅜"—End rails
2	¾ x 1⅜ x 89"—Side-rail back
2	¾ x 1⅜ x 50¾"—End-rail back
6	1 x 1⅜ x 33" pine—Support spacers
2	¾ x 1¾ x 35" pine—End-cushion supports
4	¾ x 1¾ x 34¾" pine—Side-cushion supports
2	¾ x 1⅜ x 46⅝" pine—End bed supports
2	¾ x 1⅜ x 85¾" pine—Side bed supports
1	¾ x 47¾ x 85¾" Novaply—Bed
2	¾ x 8¼ x 47⅞"—End aprons
2	¾ x 8¼ x 87⅝"—Side aprons
6	¾ x 6½ x 47⅞"—Cross members
2	¹⁄₃₂ x 7⅞ x 52"—End laminate
2	¹⁄₃₂ x 7⅞ x 88"—Side laminate
4	¾ x 6½ x 40¼"—Base
4	¾ x 4 x 8½"—Bottom pads
4	¾ x 4 x 2"—Base ends
4	¾ x 4 x 11⅛"—Base diagonals
2	¾ x 4 x 11⅞"—Base tops
8	¾ x 3¾ x 31½"—Uprights
8	¾ x 4 x 23⅞"—Upright fillers
4	¾ x 1½ x 28"—Temporary supports
1	¾ x 5 x 58⅝"—Stretcher top
1	¾ x 3½ x 58⅝"—Stretcher center
1	¾ x 3½ x 58⅝"—Stretcher bottom
2	¾ x 2⅛ x 58⅝"—Stretcher sides
18	2" angle brackets—Pockets
18	No. 8 x ½" rh screws with washers—Brackets
32	No. 8 x 1¼" fh screws
32	No. 8 x 1¼" rh screws
18	No. 8 x 1½" rh screws
20	No. 8 x 2" rh screws
18	No. 8 x 2¼" rh screws
28	No. 8 x 3½" rh screws
20	⁵⁄₁₆ x 1½" lagscrews with washers

White glue, contact cement, staples, rubber cement

5-in. mark. Grasp the cloth at one end and pull apart at the slit into two 5-in-wide strips. Cover the cushions by stapling the cloth to the rear side, a trifle above center. Pull the opposite end taut and again staple at rear of the support. Work from the center out. Be sure the staples set flush. If not, hammer them all the way home. Do likewise with the rail. Ends of the cushion cloth are cemented. Pull the cloth toward the center, then carefully cut the excess with a razor blade. Pull loose ends to the back and cement.

The support spacer is attached to the cushion support with five 2-in. rh screws in each piece. Drive the screws tightly.

● **Final assembly.** Place the support spacer under the rail and screw rail into place with 3½-in. rh screws. Force the cushion as tight as possible against the rail and attach with the 2¼-in. screws. Have an assistant help you. If you can't get 2¼-in. screws, use 2½-in. ones with several

washers under the heads to keep points from penetrating.

● **Drop pockets.** The molded-rubber pockets are made slightly oversize so they may be trimmed to fit various tables. Pockets in the kit are cut with a sharp knife or scissors. Three metal brackets hold each pocket in place, using Pop-rivets. The other end of each bracket is attached to the table with a ½-in. screw. Since bracket holes vary, no dimensions are given. If too large or too far in from edge, drill new holes as necessary. Press top of the pocket down firmly against the padded rail when positioning brackets.

Rail markers are ⅜ in. pressure-sensitive paper discs available at art and stationery shops. Peel off protective backing and press them in place. Paint the base as desired.

The kit contains four leveling jacks, 22 ft. of cushion rubber, billiard cloth, six drop pockets and a ¼ x 5 x 280-in. urethanefoam strip.

Bumper-pool table in a small space

■ POOL HAS LONG been favored as an American family pastime, but two obstacles—cost and space—have kept pool tables out of most homes. Now, by building a regulation-size bumper-pool table yourself, you too can get in on the fun of skillful pool playing.

The most important feature of a good pool table is rigidity. Our version, with its ¾-in. particleboard bed, stacks up against good commercial tables. Also, the one shown boasts aprons and legs of 5/4 (1⅛-in.) stock. Though designed so that construction is simple, quality has not been sacrificed. And, to make shopping for materials an easy task, all the specialty pool items are available by mail order.

The pool table measures 32x48 in. Some lumberyards will (and some won't) sell you the particleboard cut to size. When buying, it's important to make sure that the board is free of any warp.

Lay out the hole locations for the bumpers and drill them with a 1⅜-in. bit. Cup holes will have to be cut with a sabre saw, but before sawing them in the particleboard, check for size on a piece of scrap. When testing the cup liners for fit, drape several pieces of cloth over the holes; the fit should be fairly snug.

Apron members are cut to size next. Choice of lumber is optional but, if you plan to paint your table, a less expensive wood (such as fir) will do. If you prefer stain, consider a hardwood with an attractive grain (walnut or birch, for example). Lay out the oval ball return openings on the end panels and cut them with a sabre saw or jigsaw.

Add the cleats to the apron members, using flathead screws and glue. Position the cleats accurately as they will indirectly determine the cushion height, which is very important. Notice the counter-bored holes drilled in the cushion liner for the bed-to-liner screws.

Next, cut and assemble the legs. These are attached to the 2x3-in. frame as shown. Drill the

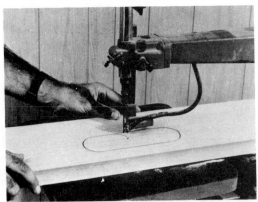

THE OVAL CUTOUT for the ball return in the end panel is made before assembly. Use a jig or sabre saw.

THE BALL-RETURN BOX is simply constructed with butt joints. The box bottom slopes slightly toward opening.

BUMPER-POOL TABLE

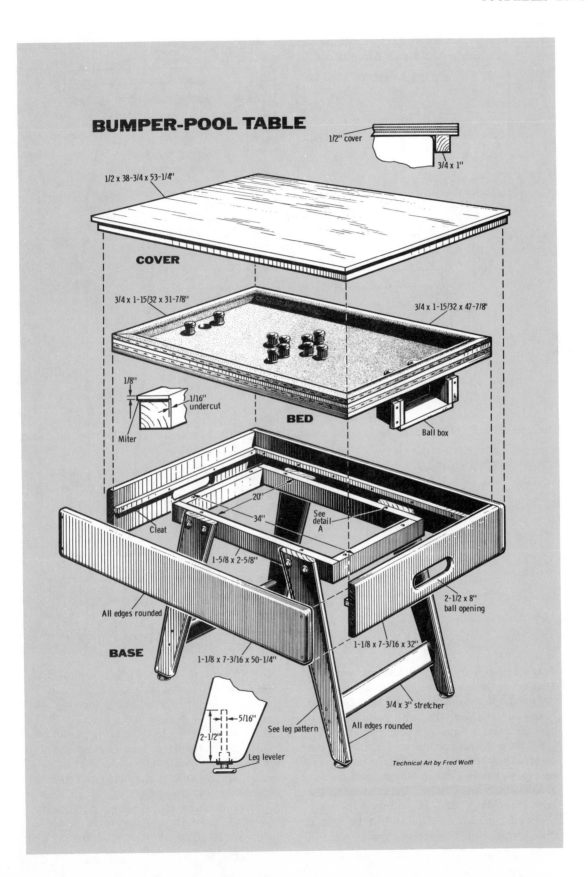

1/2" cover

3/4 x 1"

1/2 x 38-3/4 x 53-1/4"

COVER

3/4 x 1-15/32 x 31-7/8"

3/4 x 1-15/32 x 47-7/8"

1/8"

1/16" undercut

Miter

BED

Ball box

20"

See detail A

34"

Cleat

1-5/8 x 2-5/8"

1-1/8 x 7-3/16 x 32"

2-1/2 x 8" ball opening

All edges rounded

BASE

1-1/8 x 7-3/16 x 50-1/4"

3/4 x 3" stretcher

5/16"

2-1/2"

See leg pattern

All edges rounded

Leg leveler

Technical Art by Fred Wolff

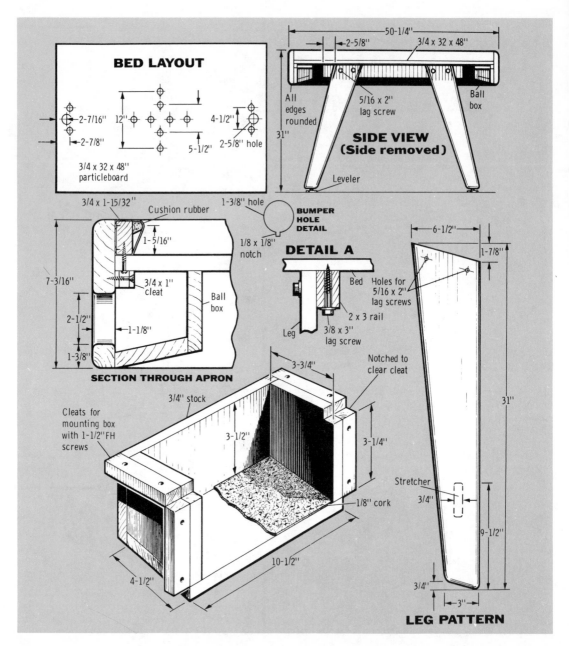

BED LAYOUT

2-7/16" 12" 4-1/2"

2-7/8" 5-1/2" 2-5/8" hole

3/4 x 32 x 48"
particleboard

50-1/4"

2-5/8" 3/4 x 32 x 48"

All
edges
rounded

5/16 x 2"
lag screw

Ball
box

31"

**SIDE VIEW
(Side removed)**

Leveler

3/4 x 1-15/32" Cushion rubber

1-3/8" hole

**BUMPER
HOLE
DETAIL**

1/8 x 1/8"
notch

1-5/16"

7-3/16"

3/4 x 1"
cleat

Ball
box

2-1/2"

1-1/8"

1-3/8"

SECTION THROUGH APRON

DETAIL A

Bed Holes for
5/16 x 2"
lag screws

2 x 3 rail

Leg 3/8 x 3"
lag screw

6-1/2"

1-7/8"

31"

Notched to
clear cleat

3-3/4"

3-1/4"

Cleats for
mounting box
with 1-1/2"FH
screws

3/4" stock

3-1/2"

1/8" cork

4-1/2"

10-1/2"

Stretcher

3/4"

9-1/2"

3/4"

3"

LEG PATTERN

clearance holes for the leg levelers and then
drive home the special Teenuts. Use lagscrews
to join the leg assembly to the bed. *Caution:*
Take care when working with particleboard—
overtightening a screw can strip the hole.

Cut the wood cushion liner to size, mitering the
corners, then undercut the ends. The undercut is
necessary to allow clearance for the gathered felt
at the ends of the cushions. After mitering the
lines, lower the blade ⅛ in. and recut the ends.

The cushions are now added. Cut the strips a
trifle longer than the liner and apply a coat of

contact cement to both surfaces. Allow this to
set, then join the pieces carefully. If you
examine the rubber in cross section, you'll
notice it has a shallow and a deep curve. The
shallow part is the top, therefore mount it ac-
cordingly to the liner. Trim ends to match the
mitered liner. Use a sharp knife, after dipping it
in water, to lubricate the blade or you'll have
trouble cutting the rubber.

Cover the cushions and bed next. If the cloth is
wrinkled, press it carefully on the *wrong* side
with a steam iron set on low. Drape the cloth

THE BED CLOTH is stapled around the perimeter every inch or so. Knife for trimming should be razor sharp.

THE CUSHION RUBBER is cut a bit oversize and attached with contact cement (see inset). Next, trim.

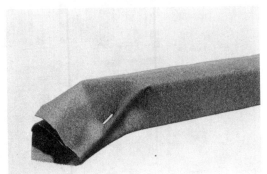

FELT IS FOLDED over the ends, and tucked beneath the undercut in the liner. Finally, staple and trim.

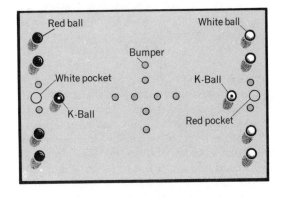

over the bed and tack with staples spaced 1 in. apart: first at the four corners, pulling the cloth taut before stapling; next along the ends, and finally along the long sides. After stapling completely around the perimeter of the bed, trim the excess cloth with a knife.

Slit the cloth over the holes with a sharp blade, stopping just short of the edges. Make eight slits in each hole area. Tap the pocket liner into place so that the edge is just a trifle below the surface. The bumpers are inserted into the holes with their projections aligned with notches of the holes and fastened with nuts.

Staple cushion covers along the back edge of the liner. Do the ends first; pull material taut, then staple at 1-in. intervals all along. Pull cloth around cushion and repeat the procedure on other edge of the cloth. Fold ends over as shown and staple gathered felt in the undercut section. Cut off excess cloth, and attach cushions to the table with roundhead screws driven from below.

Make and attach the ball boxes as shown. A plywood cover with attractive decals protects your table and completes the job.

HOW TO PLAY BUMPER POOL

Number of players: two to four. Each side has five balls: one side red, one white. In each set ball marked with spot is called the king (K) ball.

STRATEGY OF PLAY

Balls are spotted as shown above; white balls shoot toward white pocket and red toward red. To start play, both players shoot their K balls simultaneously toward their respective pockets. The player whose ball is closest to his pocket has the right to continue to shoot. After he "makes" (pockets) his K ball, he may shoot at *any* ball on the table. *Important:* Until a player makes his K ball, he may shoot only for his pocket; he may not try to hit his opponent's ball.

SKILLFUL PLAY

The strategy is to keep your opponent from having an open shot at his pocket while you leave yourself open to shoot at your pocket. This is usually done either by knocking your opponent's ball out of position, or by positioning your own ball in such a manner as to block his shot. The player who pockets his five balls first wins.

PENALTIES

If a player sinks one of his balls before the K ball, opponent pockets any two balls and shoots.

If a player causes a ball to jump the table, his opponent places the jumped ball wherever he chooses (including in the center of the eight-bumper cluster), pockets any two balls and shoots.

If a player pockets an opponent's ball, it is a scratch and he loses his turn. The pocketed ball stays in the pocket.

Porch with a double deck adds two party rooms

■ THE DOUBLE-DECK porch extends the living space on both floors of this home. With sliding doors of the first-floor porch open, the adjoining living room doubles in size. The second-floor master bedroom has a panoramic view through the doors of its adjoining upper deck.

Several considerations were included in designing the two-level space: First, the structure had to blend with the American colonial house. Second, we wanted to employ the newest construction materials and design ideas. Third, we wanted to join the deck and porch with a stairway fitting the design scheme. Fourth, the porch had to be as open as possible for summer enjoy-

GALVANIZED spiral stairway joins the two levels for convenient back-and-forth traffic.

UPPER-LEVEL sundeck is a delightful vantage point for surveying the scenery while sunning, having lunch or entertaining guests. For evening entertaining, you might prefer moving downstairs to the screened-in room. It has an open, airy feeling, yet it's near the kitchen and living room. The room has window panels that seal it for use during cold weather.

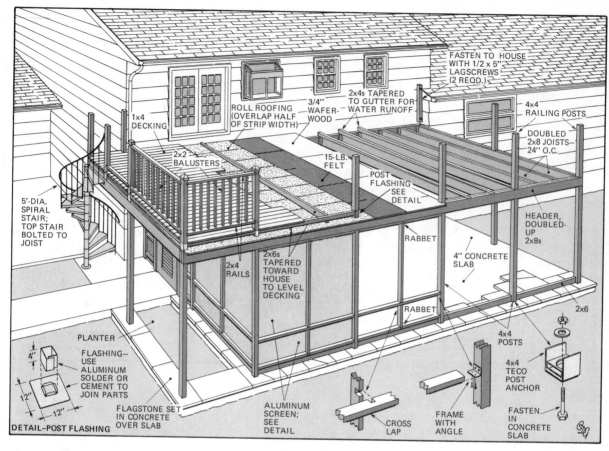

FASTEN TO HOUSE WITH 1/2 x 5" LAGSCREWS (2 REQD.)

1x4 DECKING

ROLL ROOFING (OVERLAP HALF OF STRIP WIDTH)

3/4" WAFER-WOOD

2x4s TAPERED TO GUTTER FOR WATER RUNOFF

4x4 RAILING POSTS

2x2 BALUSTERS

15-LB. FELT

DOUBLED 2x8 JOISTS—24" O.C.

POST FLASHING SEE DETAIL

5'-DIA. SPIRAL STAIR; TOP STAIR BOLTED TO JOIST

HEADER, DOUBLED-UP 2x8s

RABBET

4" CONCRETE SLAB

2x4 RAILS

2x6s TAPERED TOWARD HOUSE TO LEVEL DECKING

2x6

RABBET

4x4 POSTS

PLANTER

FLASHING— USE ALUMINUM SOLDER OR CEMENT TO JOIN PARTS

4"

12"

12"

DETAIL–POST FLASHING

FLAGSTONE SET IN CONCRETE OVER SLAB

ALUMINUM SCREEN; SEE DETAIL

CROSS LAP

FRAME WITH ANGLE

4x4 TECO POST ANCHOR

FASTEN IN CONCRETE SLAB

ment, yet enclosed for cold-weather use. Fifth, the porch/deck needed a lighting system.

To maintain the colonial feeling, we gave the deck an open look with railings made of simple 2x2 balusters between posts. Hinged French doors with grille inserts give a multipaned colo-

nial look. Several relatively new design features and materials include: a window greenhouse, decay-resistant, pressure-treated wood, metal construction connectors for strong joints; roof sheathing and finished ceiling panels of particleboard. To join the two spaces, one side of the deck overhangs the

SUPPORT POSTS and joists are the only framing members installed in this view. Note the temporary diagonal bracing on the posts at this stage.

FRAMING OF the lower porch is complete in this view. The railing posts on the upper deck are in place and the roll roofing has been installed.

THE DETAIL (far left) shows two upper rails joining a capped post. Detail (near left) shows metal post-and-beam tie. Note corner of joist hanger (top left in photo).

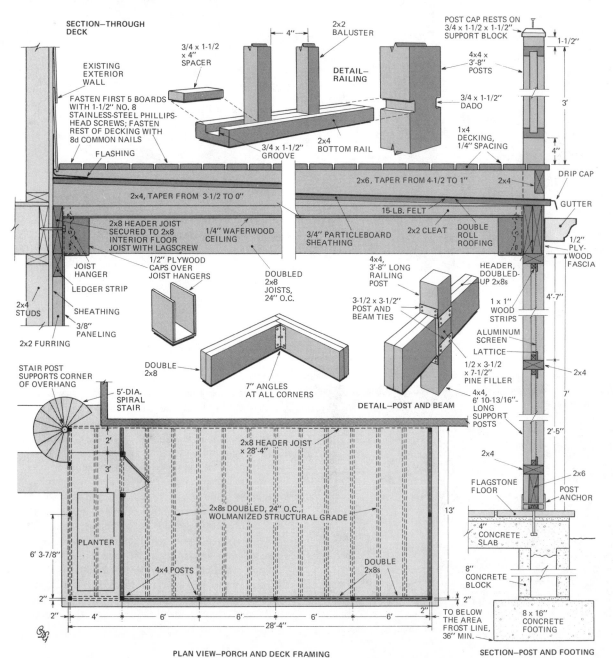

SECTION—THROUGH DECK

EXISTING EXTERIOR WALL

FASTEN FIRST 5 BOARDS WITH 1-1/2" NO. 8 STAINLESS-STEEL PHILLIPS-HEAD SCREWS; FASTEN REST OF DECKING WITH 8d COMMON NAILS

FLASHING

3/4 x 1-1/2 x 4" SPACER

2x2 BALUSTER

4"

DETAIL—RAILING

3/4 x 1-1/2" GROOVE

2x4 BOTTOM RAIL

3/4 x 1-1/2" DADO

POST CAP RESTS ON 3/4 x 1-1/2 x 1-1/2" SUPPORT BLOCK

1-1/2"

4x4 x 3'-8" POSTS

3'

1x4 DECKING, 1/4" SPACING

4"

DRIP CAP

2x4, TAPER FROM 3-1/2 TO 0"

2x6, TAPER FROM 4-1/2 TO 1"

2x4

GUTTER

15-LB. FELT

2x8 HEADER JOIST SECURED TO 2x8 INTERIOR FLOOR JOIST WITH LAGSCREW

1/4" WAFERWOOD CEILING

3/4" PARTICLEBOARD SHEATHING

2x2 CLEAT

DOUBLE ROLL ROOFING

1/2" PLYWOOD FASCIA

JOIST HANGER

1/2" PLYWOOD CAPS OVER JOIST HANGERS

DOUBLED 2x8 JOISTS, 24" O.C.

4x4, 3'-8" LONG RAILING POST

HEADER, DOUBLED-UP 2x8s

LEDGER STRIP

SHEATHING

3-1/2 x 3-1/2" POST AND BEAM TIES

1 x 1" WOOD STRIPS

4'-7"

2x4 STUDS

3/8" PANELING

ALUMINUM SCREEN

2x2 FURRING

DOUBLE 2x8

7" ANGLES AT ALL CORNERS

LATTICE

1/2 x 3-1/2 x 7-1/2" PINE FILLER

DETAIL—POST AND BEAM

4x4, 6' 10-13/16" LONG SUPPORT POSTS

2x4

7'

STAIR POST SUPPORTS CORNER OF OVERHANG

5'-DIA. SPIRAL STAIR

2'

2'-5"

2x4

2x8 HEADER JOIST x 28'-4"

13'

FLAGSTONE FLOOR

2x6

POST ANCHOR

3'

2x8s DOUBLED, 24" O.C., WOLMANIZED STRUCTURAL GRADE

4" CONCRETE SLAB

PLANTER

6' 3-7/8"

4x4 POSTS

DOUBLE 2x8s

8" CONCRETE BLOCK

2"

2"

4'

6'

6'

6'

6'

2"

2"

TO BELOW THE AREA FROST LINE, 36" MIN.

8 x 16" CONCRETE FOOTING

28'-4"

PLAN VIEW—PORCH AND DECK FRAMING

SECTION—POST AND FOOTING

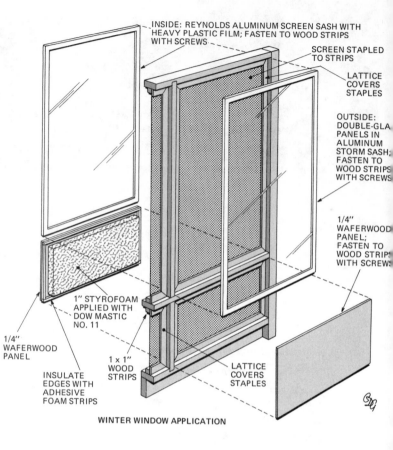

INSIDE: REYNOLDS ALUMINUM SCREEN SASH WITH HEAVY PLASTIC FILM; FASTEN TO WOOD STRIPS WITH SCREWS

SCREEN STAPLED TO STRIPS

LATTICE COVERS STAPLES

OUTSIDE: DOUBLE-GLA PANELS IN ALUMINUM STORM SASH; FASTEN TO WOOD STRIPS WITH SCREWS

1/4" WAFERWOOD PANEL; FASTEN TO WOOD STRIPS WITH SCREWS

1" STYROFOAM APPLIED WITH DOW MASTIC NO. 11

1/4" WAFERWOOD PANEL

INSULATE EDGES WITH ADHESIVE FOAM STRIPS

1 x 1" WOOD STRIPS

LATTICE COVERS STAPLES

WINTER WINDOW APPLICATION

WINTERIZING porch includes fastening particleboard over lower windows. Panel is secured with screws through each edge of panel into a wood strip.

SLIDING PATIO DOOR leads to living room. Stationary window (center) lets light in. "Winter windows" and space heater prepare porch for cold weather.

porch and neatly accommodates a spiral stairway.

For minimal obstruction to the view, the enclosed porch has a series of windows—the space between each pair of posts is framed into two larger windows on top and two smaller windows directly below; yet permanent screens ensure protection from insects. For cooler times, storm windows made in the shop using bronze-finished aluminum sash are applied over the upper porch windows and fastened in place with screws. Screened openings at the floor are covered from the outside with particleboard panels. During the coldest weather, interior storm windows of PVC film in aluminum sash are applied to the upper windows; interior particleboard panels backed with polystyrene insulation cover the lower openings.

Our night lighting system includes mushroom lights for the walkways and a spotlight on the deck.

The concrete slab and flagstone floor on top were already in place. If you must begin by pouring footings and a concrete slab, any good reference book on concrete should provide the necessary information to do this job correctly.

Locating the header joist

Lay out the header joist along the house wall. If you have access to the deck from the second level, position the header joist so the finished decking will be 2 to 3 in. below the sill of the doorway to the house. In this case, the center of the joist should be about 12 to 13 in. below the proposed sill to allow for decking, tapered boards and roofing materials. Make sure the header joist is level by snapping a level chalkline along the house where the top of the header joist will be.

Strip away siding or shingles so the header can be installed flush against the sheathing and re-snap the level chalkline on the sheathing. Also remove siding to attach the two adjacent posts to the house studs with 6-in. lagscrews. Resnap the vertical chalklines; use a spirit level to ensure that the lines are plumb and level. Run a bead of caulk along the chalkline. Lagscrew header to second-floor joist header. Apply aluminum flashing over the sheathing and lap it on the header.

At each post location, bore an oversize hole through the flagstone into the concrete for a bolt to secure the post anchor bracket. Secure the bolt with patching cement. Slip the bracket over the bolt and secure it with a washer and nut. Set the post in the anchor. Secure the post with nails through predrilled holes on the bracket. Brace posts with two diagonal 2x4s until framing is done.

Lay out locations of the rail-post fasteners on the header joists. Install the joist hanger hardware. Then measure, cut and fasten joists to posts with metal post-and-beam connections. You must use a ½-in. pine filler between posts with the connector.

Putting in the stairway

The spiral stair post supports a corner of the deck overhang. Erect the stairway at this point and fasten it in place. We bolted the top step to the joist.

Next, cut posts for the deck railing to size. Cut dadoes for top and bottom rails; install posts in

metal connectors already placed.

To finish the ceiling, we nailed 2x2 cleats near the top of the joists; then fastened ¼-in. particleboard panels to the cleats.

After framing porch windows, we nailed 1x1-in. strips around each frame and used heavy-duty, galvanized staples to fasten screening permanently to the strips. Lattice strips cover the staples.

For proper drainage of the deck level, we attached 2x4s cut on a skew (to direct water to the rain gutter) to the joists. Over this we fastened ¾-in. particleboard sheathing with panels staggered to avoid any long seams.

Then we applied 15-lb. roofing felt (tarpaper) parallel to the house wall. Each layer should overlap the preceding one 12 in., starting at the lower edge. Next, we installed 30-lb. mineral roll roofing, sealing it with asphalt cement. Each strip laps the upper half of the previous strip to get a double thickness over the deck.

The next step is to flash the railing posts. Solder the two-part aluminum flashing together or join with plastic cement.

Leveling the surface

To level the deck surface, we positioned 2x6s tapering toward the house. Space the 2x6s 24 in. on centers; temporarily tack some 1x4 decking on top of them to hold position. When they are set, begin to nail decking at the railing; work toward the house, staggering the joints.

To avoid splitting, prebore 1x4 decking for fasteners, especially near edges. Trim board ends after nailing deck to ensure a straight line.

The deck railing has 2x4 top and bottom rails between posts with 2x2 balusters 4 in. apart. Using a circular saw, cut baluster grooves centered the length of each rail. Cut balusters to length, test-fit then assemble rails and balusters with resorcinol glue and 6d galvanized nails. Install 4-in. spacers between balusters on the bottom rail to fill the groove, then the railing sections between posts, and finally the post-cap support blocks and caps.

We wanted to stain the lumber a rich brown, but we had to wait six months to let salts leach out.

In the meantime, you can work on the window treatments (see winter window application drawing). An indoor-outdoor porch like ours is sure to increase your enjoyment of the outdoors and encourage you to entertain.

Screened porch you can add

■ WHEN IT COMES to practical outdoor living, you just can't beat a screened porch. Open patios are fine when there are no bugs or sudden showers, but one or the other can ruin a cookout. When you're safe from both within the shelter of a screened porch, summer entertaining and living become twice the fun for family and guests alike.

Adding such a porch is not the major job you may think. It's a project that can be completed in stages to suit both your spare time and wallet. And even before you have it fully screened in, you'll find it usable for a cookout without worrying about getting wet.

The best spot for your porch is at the back of the house where you have the most privacy, but more important, where it will be accessible from the kitchen. If you are able to build it on the north side of the house, it will be shaded from the hot afternoon sun.

You can tackle the job in three easy stages; 1. Pouring the slab; 2. Framing the roof; 3. Adding the screens, all of which you can do yourself with help now and then from a friend. In most cases you'll be ahead if you have the slab poured. In time saved, you can have your porch completed over a two-week vacation.

If you take on the slab yourself, stake it out to suit and remove 5 or 6 in. of topsoil. Dig down 18 in. along the outer edges to form a trench to provide extra support for the roof. Erect form boards so the slab will pitch slightly away from the house (¼-in. per ft.) and are level with foundation.

Regardless of size, it's best to pour the slab in sections, a day apart. This minimizes cracking and makes it possible, when working alone, to trowel the concrete before it sets. As each divider is pulled out, a ½x4-in. strip of expansion felt is tacked to the green section before pouring the next. When the slab is finished, cover it with building paper or burlap and keep it wet for four or five days, allowing the concrete to cure fully.

Before you start the roof, study the framing drawing. Each rafter is paired with a ceiling joist and the joists are faced on the underside with ⅜-in. plywood before a lintel, supported by 4x4 posts, is placed under it.

Start by spiking a 2x6 nailer to the side of the house at ceiling height. This runs the full length of the porch. Next erect a box-like frame around three sides and prop it up temporarily in a level position. Now install the ceiling joists, 24 in. center to center, and toenail them to the nailer. Spike them through at the front. After this, figure how many rafters are needed (two more than joists if you double up the end ones to make a flush surface) and cut one for a pattern. Taper the end to match the pitch of the house roof. Nail

IF BUGS AND RAIN send you scurrying indoors from a cookout, it may be time to consider a screened porch.

SLOPE THE FORM 2 in. to assure proper drainage. Then divide the form in sections for pouring.

AFTER EACH SECTION is poured, smooth it with a trowel, then cover it with burlap and keep it moist.

CEILING JOISTS are toenailed to a 2x6 nailer which is first nailed to the house at ceiling height.

CEILING FRAMING is temporarily supported in a level position by scrap props which rest on the slab.

rafters to the roof, right on top of the existing shingles, and spike them to the joists.

Next, you close in the framing by nailing ¾-in. plywood to the rafters and ⅜-in. plywood to the joists. Follow this by covering the roof with tar paper, then with a metal flashing where the new roof meets the old and, finally, with shingles to match the house. All that's left is to install the 4x4 lintel and its supporting 4x4 posts before filling in the ends of the porch roof and adding a 1x8 fascia board across the front and up the ends.

The number and size of frames you need to enclose your porch is determined from the porch itself. If you've planned for 8 ft. between posts, then all screens across the front can be made 48 in. wide. The drawing shows how the screen frames are made from common 1⅛-in. screen stock. Note how members are half-lapped for extra strength.

You have a choice of installing the frames permanently in place or fitting them so they can be lifted out and stored for the winter. In the

TAPERED ENDS of the rafters rest on the roof, to which they're nailed 24 in. o.c. Plywood covers rafters.

WHEN WIRING IS IN, the underside of the joists is covered with ⅜-in. plywood.

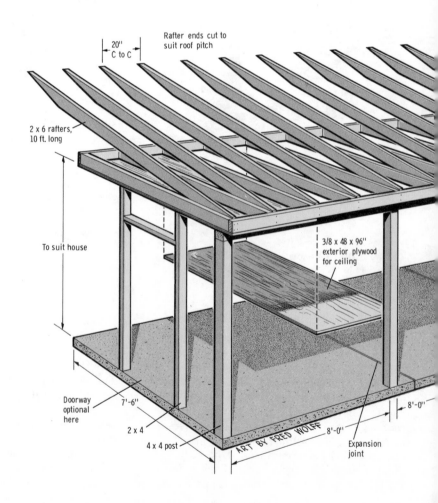

20"
C to C

Rafter ends cut to suit roof pitch

2 x 6 rafters, 10 ft. long

3/8 x 48 x 96" exterior plywood for ceiling

To suit house

Doorway optional here

7'-6"

2 x 4

4 x 4 post

ART BY FRED WOLFF

8'-0"

8'-0"

Expansion joint

PERMANENT 4x4 posts are anchored to the slab with angle brackets, then a 4x4 lintel is placed on top.

AFTER ADDING FLASHING, roof sheathing is covered with felt, and matching shingles are applied.

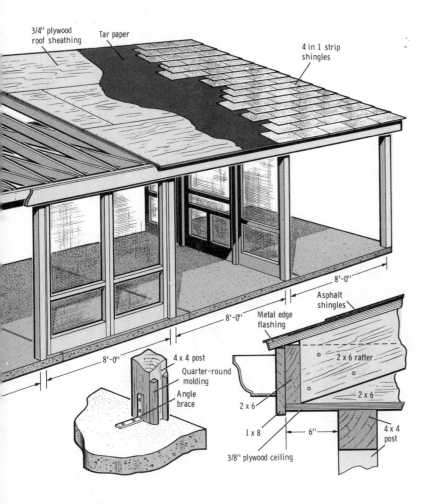

3/4" plywood roof sheathing

Tar paper

4 in 1 strip shingles

8'-0"

8'-0"

8'-0"

Asphalt shingles

Metal edge flashing

4 x 4 post

Quarter-round molding

Angle brace

2 x 6

1 x 8

6"

2 x 6 rafter

2 x 6

4 x 4 post

3/8" plywood ceiling

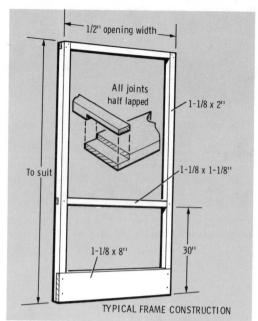

1/2" opening width

All joints
half lapped

1-1/8 x 2"

To suit

1-1/8 x 1-1/8"

1-1/8 x 8"   30"

TYPICAL FRAME CONSTRUCTION

SCREEN FRAMES are built with half-lap joints for strength. Make two frames for each 8-ft. opening.

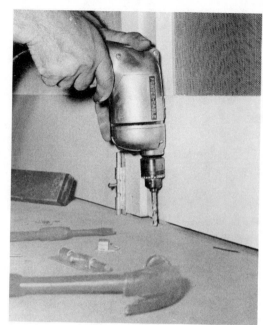

SLIDING-DOOR BOLTS lock screens to the slab. Use a masonry bit to drill holes in the slab.

latter case, door bolts are added to the bottom rails to engage holes drilled in the slab. Quarter-round molding nailed to the posts and lintel makes the screens fit bug-tight. Drain notches should be provided along the bottoms of the screens, and if screens are permanently installed, pick copper wire or aluminum, or one of the new plastic screening materials, to cover them.

The door opening in the end of the porch is framed with 2x4s which are anchored to the slab and the joist with angle brackets. You can buy a stock door as cheaply as you can make it. The area which surrounds the doorway is fitted with individual screens.

As the summer goes by you'll enjoy your porch more and more. You'll find it one of the best investments you can make for a small home.

QUARTER-ROUND MOLDING, tacked to posts and lintel, provides neat rabbets in which screens rest.

THE DOORWAY is framed in the end with 2x4s for a stock door. Openings around the door are screened.

THE BUG-FREE party room shown gives all the advantages of outdoor living plus protection from the weather. Whenever it rains, the garage doors still close.

Screened porch from your garage

■ A QUICK, INEXPENSIVE WAY to gain a closed-in porch or patio is simply to screen an existing garage. Though an attached garage is more desirable for this improvement, there's no reason the idea cannot be adapted to a detached one. Either way, you will gain by giving those noisy, sometimes clutter-prone, bored youngsters a place to play on a rainy day or create a spot for you to get away from it all.

The garage shown has a 15-ft.-wide door opening. The screened wall is laid out in six panels, including the convenience door at one end. A 24-in. fan is installed in the wall between the house and the garage. The screened opening is ample for drawing cool, evening breezes into the house without airconditioning.

Before starting on the project, make certain that the garage-door handle projects no farther than the garage door stops. Then lay the sole plate along the garage-door opening and line it up with the stops on the *inside*. This is fastened with flat-head wood screws into lead anchors dropped into the concrete. When you disassemble the setup, the plugs can be filled with corks to prevent them from becoming clogged with dirt.

Divide your garage opening into panels 30 to 40 in. wide for best-looking results. The entrance door is optional, but it is well worth the small amount of effort that building it requires. For rigidity, use a 2 x 2 for the door post (on the hinged side), fastening it at the top and bottom with L-shaped brackets and screws.

Redwood is used throughout on the porch shown. It can be stained natural or painted to suit your preference.

Caution: Since there's a more than even chance your garage finished opening may be out of plumb or not level, trim and fit the individual screens to their exact position in sequence. Link each screen to its neighbor as shown in the drawings. To save yourself some frustration next spring when putting them back up, number the screens for easy identification and quick placement.

If you decide to paint your screens, the finished job will look neater if you do all the carpentry first, including temporary assembly. Then take them down, prime and paint the wood, and fasten the wire screening.

For wrinkle-free screens, use the time-tested method of shimming both ends and clamping the middle before stapling the screening to the framework. To finish, cover the staples with conventional screen molding.

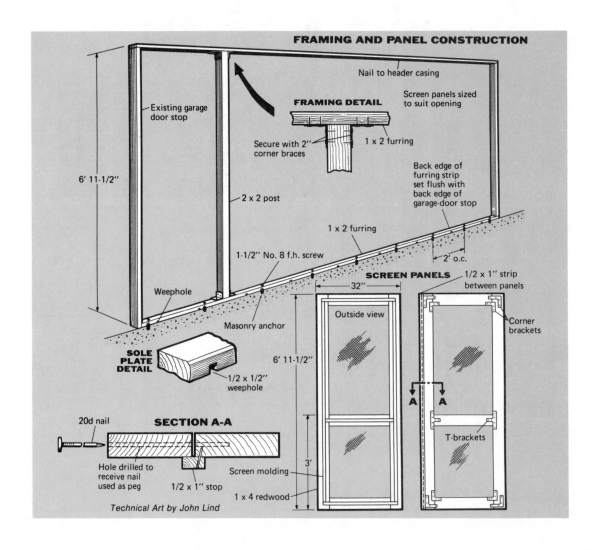

FRAMING AND PANEL CONSTRUCTION

Nail to header casing

Screen panels sized to suit opening

FRAMING DETAIL

Existing garage door stop

1 x 2 furring

Secure with 2'' corner braces

Back edge of furring strip set flush with back edge of garage-door stop

6' 11-1/2''

2 x 2 post

1 x 2 furring

1-1/2'' No. 8 f.h. screw

2' o.c.

SCREEN PANELS

1/2 x 1'' strip between panels

32''

Weephole

Corner brackets

Masonry anchor

Outside view

SOLE PLATE DETAIL

1/2 x 1/2'' weephole

6' 11-1/2''

T-brackets

A   A

20d nail

SECTION A-A

Hole drilled to receive nail used as peg

1/2 x 1'' stop

3'

Screen molding

1 x 4 redwood

Technical Art by John Lind

Old-time porch swing

■ YOUR ENTIRE FAMILY from grandparents to toddlers are sure to enjoy sitting and relaxing in our version of the old-fashioned, front-porch swing.

If you own a porch you can suspend the swing from stout hardware anchored in the porch rafters or joists. Happily, those who live in today's modern porchless houses can enjoy this swing too

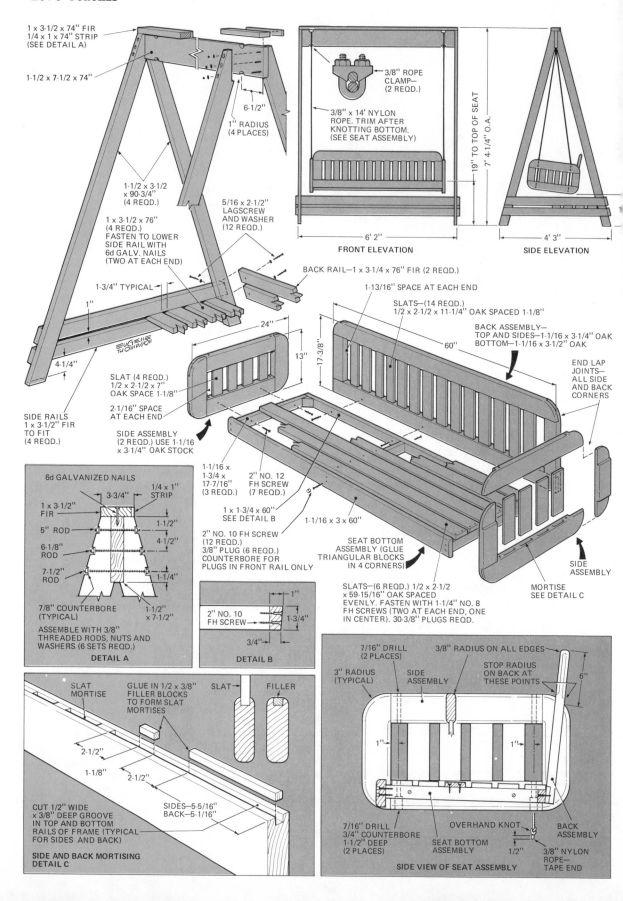

1 x 3-1/2 x 74" FIR
1/4 x 1 x 74" STRIP
(SEE DETAIL A)

1-1/2 x 7-1/2 x 74"

6-1/2"

1" RADIUS
(4 PLACES)

1-1/2 x 3-1/2
x 90-3/4"
(4 REQD.)

1 x 3-1/2 x 76"
(4 REQD.)
FASTEN TO LOWER
SIDE RAIL WITH
6d GALV. NAILS
(TWO AT EACH END)

5/16 x 2-1/2"
LAGSCREW
AND WASHER
(12 REQD.)

1-3/4" TYPICAL

1"

4-1/4"

SIDE RAILS
1 x 3-1/2" FIR
TO FIT
(4 REQD.)

BACK RAIL—1 x 3-1/4 x 76" FIR (2 REQD.)

24"

13"

SLAT (4 REQD.)
1/2 x 2-1/2 x 7"
OAK SPACE 1-1/8"

2-1/16" SPACE
AT EACH END

SIDE ASSEMBLY
(2 REQD.) USE 1-1/16
x 3-1/4" OAK STOCK

3/8" ROPE
CLAMP—
(2 REQD.)

3/8" x 14' NYLON
ROPE. TRIM AFTER
KNOTTING BOTTOM.
(SEE SEAT ASSEMBLY)

19" TO TOP OF SEAT

7' 4-1/4" O.A.

6' 2"

FRONT ELEVATION

4' 3"

SIDE ELEVATION

1-13/16" SPACE AT EACH END

SLATS—(14 REQD.)
1/2 x 2-1/2 x 11-1/4" OAK SPACED 1-1/8"

BACK ASSEMBLY—
TOP AND SIDES—1-1/16 x 3-1/4" OAK
BOTTOM—1-1/16 x 3-1/2" OAK

60"

17-3/8"

END LAP
JOINTS—
ALL SIDE
AND BACK
CORNERS

1-1/16 x
1-3/4 x
17-7/16"
(3 REQD.)

2" NO. 12
FH SCREW
(7 REQD.)

1 x 1-3/4 x 60"
SEE DETAIL B

2" NO. 10 FH SCREW
(12 REQD.)
3/8" PLUG (6 REQD.)
COUNTERBORE FOR
PLUGS IN FRONT RAIL ONLY

1-1/16 x 3 x 60"

SEAT BOTTOM
ASSEMBLY (GLUE
TRIANGULAR BLOCKS
IN 4 CORNERS)

SLATS—(6 REQD.) 1/2 x 2-1/2
x 59-15/16" OAK SPACED
EVENLY. FASTEN WITH 1-1/4" NO. 8
FH SCREWS (TWO AT EACH END, ONE
IN CENTER). 30-3/8" PLUGS REQD.

SIDE
ASSEMBLY

MORTISE
SEE DETAIL C

DETAIL A

6d GALVANIZED NAILS

3-3/4"

1/4 x 1"
STRIP

1 x 3-1/2"
FIR

5" ROD

1-1/2"

6-1/8"
ROD

4-1/2"

7-1/2"
ROD

1-1/4"

7/8" COUNTERBORE
(TYPICAL)

1-1/2"
x 7-1/2"

ASSEMBLE WITH 3/8"
THREADED RODS, NUTS AND
WASHERS (6 SETS REQD.)

DETAIL B

1"

2" NO. 10
FH SCREW

1-3/4"

3/4"

**SIDE AND BACK MORTISING
DETAIL C**

SLAT
MORTISE

GLUE IN 1/2 x 3/8"
FILLER BLOCKS
TO FORM SLAT
MORTISES

SLAT

FILLER

2-1/2"

1-1/8"

2-1/2"

SIDES—5-5/16"
BACK—5-1/16"

CUT 1/2" WIDE
x 3/8" DEEP GROOVE
IN TOP AND BOTTOM
RAILS OF FRAME (TYPICAL
FOR SIDES AND BACK)

7/16" DRILL
(2 PLACES)

3/8" RADIUS ON ALL EDGES

3" RADIUS
(TYPICAL)

SIDE
ASSEMBLY

STOP RADIUS
ON BACK AT
THESE POINTS

6"

1"

1"

7/16" DRILL
3/4" COUNTERBORE
1-1/2" DEEP
(2 PLACES)

SEAT BOTTOM
ASSEMBLY

OVERHAND KNOT

1/2"

BACK
ASSEMBLY

3/8" NYLON
ROPE—
TAPE END

SIDE VIEW OF SEAT ASSEMBLY

because we've created an alternate suspension system—a sturdy A-frame whose design blends beautifully with that of the swing. This frame allows you to set up your swing in a garden, on a patio, or anywhere in your yard the family gathers.

Starting construction

The seat section of the swing has been designed and constructed like a fine piece of furniture—quality joinery, weatherproof glue joints and plugged-over screwheads are used throughout. The seat is built of 5/4 and 1/2-in. oak while the A-frame is built of lower-cost 2x4 and 2x8 construction-grade fir. We selected clear 1x4 flooring for all horizontal frame members because it measures a full 3½ in. wide and its thickness gives more rigidity than does 3/4-in. stock.

More often than not, you will find that hardwood comes from the lumberyard surfaced on two sides only (S2S). When the lumber comes this way, you must use either a plane or jointer to joint one edge perfectly smooth and straight. You can then rip the boards (using either a radial-arm or table saw) to the widths required for the seat back and side sections. We used red oak for the seat—5/4-in. stock for all parts except the slats, which are of 1/2-in. stock.

Caution: when you go to buy your lumber, be selective; it is almost impossible to perform accurate grooving and lap-jointing on stock that is warped.

Cut scrap slats

Use your saw and a dado cutterhead to cut the grooves in the back and side section rails to receive the slats. Notice that we installed filler blocks in the grooves to get accurate and neat mortises for the slats. Cut several scrap slats to act as guides to mark the spacing for the actual slats. Cut the filler blocks out of 1/2-in.-sq. stock—which will project a hair above the surface after installation to permit flush trimming later, after gluing. Set the blocks in place with dummy slats and mark the glue border-lines (Photo 2). Mix some resorcinol (waterproof) glue and apply it sparingly to mating surfaces—don't make it too watery or it will ooze into the grooves and require difficult cleanup later.

If the blocks are snug fitting as they should be, clamping will not be necessary. Proceed down the rail installing blocks, with the aid of dummy spacers, as you go. Next day when the glue is dry, trim off the 1/8-in. projection by ripping with a smooth blade in the table saw.

Holes for the ropes

At this stage you should bore the holes for the nylon rope. The top racks get 7/16-in.-dia. holes while the lower members are counter bored to receive the knots. Make certain that you bore the larger, 3/4-in.-dia. hole first and then the 7/16-in. hole. If you reverse this order you will have great difficulty centering the holes. A drill press is almost essential for this operation to ensure that the holes pass straight through the sides.

To mark the frame members for end lap joints, clamp the sections together. Then use either a knife or a very sharp pencil to mark the cutting lines. Set the saw's dado head for a wide cut and its elevation so that the cutters will penetrate half the thickness of the stock. It's a good idea to check a test joint in scrap stock so that you are certain to produce perfectly mated end lap joints. For greatest accuracy when you're making an end lap joint, cut the first one completely and then use it as the marking guide for its mating cut.

Next, you should assemble the units temporarily to check the distance between the mortise bottoms and cut the slats to suit. Make it a point to cut the slats about 1/16 in. shorter than the actual distance to allow for the glue. Cut the slats, and then break all sharp corners on them using a Surform plane and fine sandpaper. Set the slats aside.

Rounding the edges

Before you can glue the slats in place you must round the inside edges of the frame sections with a router; this cannot be done once the slats are installed. Since the mortised inside edges will not give the router cutter's pilot guide a true surface to ride against, a simple woodworking trick is called for. Temporarily assemble the sections without slats (using tacks only at corners in the waste area, where the outside corner radius will be cut). Then cut strips of 1/8-in. hardboard equal in width to the thickness of the stock and place them around the frame inside to provide a smooth, flat surface for the router bit (Photo 7). You would be wise to set up a test strip and make a trial cut using a 3/8-in. rounding-over bit. Adjust the depth-of-cut so that it doesn't reach the mortise.

Sand all edges

While sections are still temporarily assembled, sand the insides as well as all the rounded edges.

1 TOP and bottom rails are grooved to receive slats.

2 USE DUMMY slats to locate filler blocks; mark glue border lines.

3 AFTER GLUE dries, trim the rails slightly on the saw.

7 TACK FRAME together; insert ⅛-in. strips for router guide.

8 ROUND corners using ⅜-in. bit set not to reach mortises.

9 PUT SLATS in grooves using glue; apply glue to lap joints.

13 CUT mitered ends with saw miter gauge at 15°.

14 TO CUT the long notch, clamp a 2x4 to the saw table.

15 USE holesaw in drill and a scrap block to bore notches.

It's easier to do this before the slats are in place. Make light match marks on the mating parts and then disassemble the units.

To install slats, apply glue sparingly in recesses and to the end surface of the slats. Insert all slats into one rail, apply glue to the second rail and push it onto the slats. Apply glue to the lap joints and complete the frame assembly. Hold the sections secure and square with bar clamps until the glue dries.

The seat frame is made separately. Cut the parts to size and assemble them with glue and screws as shown. Counterbore the screwholes at the front so that the screwheads can be concealed

4 BORE holes for rope. In bottom, drill larger holes first.

5 CLAMP parts to find exact dimensions for end lap joints.

6 CUT LAPS with dado head in radial or table saw.

10 USE sabre saw to cut radius on corners and round with a router.

11 CLAMP seat frame to side and back while you bore pilot holes.

12 LAY frame members on floor. Mark at 105° for miter cuts.

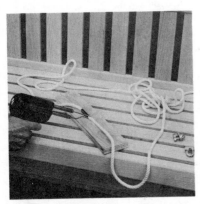

16 TO PREVENT unraveling, cut rope with a soldering gun.

17 PROP SEAT on horses to install the rope.

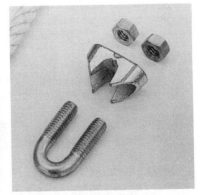

18 WEATHERPROOF clamps are available from marine houses.

with plugs cut from the oak stock. If you don't own a plug cutter, you can use maple dowels. Before you glue the seat slats in place, clamp the seat frame to the back and sides and bore the required screw holes. Two screws go into the sides from the end of the seat frame, three from the back and two from the outside of the side panel into the side of the seat back. These are sunk and plugged.

Making the A-frame

Start with the 2x4 verticals. Lay them out as shown in the photos and mark the miter cuts. Cut the miters using a radial or portable circular saw.

Next, cut the 2x8 to length and cut the half-circles for the rope near each end. For perfectly accurate notches, use a hole saw as we did (Photo 15). Since the standard hole saw only penetrates to about ¾ in., you will have to drill from both sides and then complete the cut with a sabre saw. Use a drum sander to smooth the cut. Mark locations for the ⅜-in. bolt holes, then use a 1-in. bit to bore a partial hole parallel to the flat surface of the notch, just deep enough to seat the washer. Then bore ⁷⁄₁₆-in.-dia. holes through the assembly. This is best accomplished with a helper. Lay the 2x4s on the side with the 2x8 held vertically in place between the notches. Do this on 2x4 scraps on edge to permit access with your electric drill. But, if you mark the bolt holes carefully and then support each member in proper position on the drill press, you can bore the holes individually on the separate pieces.

Since lagbolts are not available in the size required, you will have to use threaded rod cut to size, with nuts and washers at both ends. (Oversize lagbolts will not have sufficient thread to allow cutting to length.)

Assembling the frame

Assemble the frame by bolting the tops, then attach the three lower outer rails. Before you add the second rails, nail in the four horizontals using two hot-dipped galvanized nails at both ends.

To hang the seat, set it in place on high sawhorses or other support. Pass the nylon rope through the 2x8 half hole, then through the chair sides. Make an overhand knot at each end, then wrap a piece of plastic tape tightly around the rope just below the knots. *Do not cut off the waste with a knife or scissors or it will unravel.* Instead cut by burning it through with a soldering gun or heat knife. The heat will melt the end and prevent unraveling. Melted nylon will mess up the gun tip a bit, but can be cleaned off with a light sanding after the gun cools.

Adjusting the seat

The knot will seem too big to fit the ¾-in. hole, but can be forced in if you pull hard enough. The fit will be good and snug so you won't need a washer. Remove the supports and let the seat hang, then attach the special rope clamps at the top. The seat can be adjusted to any angle you want and locked in position by tightening the clamps. Most people prefer to have the seat of the swing tipped slightly to the back. Although this makes it a little harder to get out of the swing, you don't have the feeling you will be sent off the front edge when you start swinging. Do some experimentation to determine which position is most comfortable for you.

Finishing the swing

Very little work is required for finishing the swing; we simply applied three coats of exterior urethane to the new wood following the manufacturer's instructions on the can. Since the swing itself is of oak, however, its parts must first be rubbed with natural paste wood filler to fill the wood's open pores. Using turpentine, thin the filler to a creamlike consistency and brush it on—first against and then with the grain. Let the filler set until it turns flat, then rub off all excess filler with burlap or other coarse-textured cloth. Wait 24 hours before applying the first coat of finish. (Note: *You do not need to use the filler on the close-grain fir used in the A-frame*).

Alternate suspension method

Those who have a porch will want to hang the swing from its ceiling rather than build the A-frame. You can suspend the swing from two ⅜ x 4½-in. screw eyes turned into one or two ceiling joists. (If the ceiling joists run parallel to the swing's length, both screw eyes will be in one joist. If joists run perpendicular to the swing, each screw eye will be in its own joist.) Locate joists using a small nail. When a joist is located, bore several small holes to make certain that the screw eye will go into the center of the joist.

Some additional hardware is necessary for a ceiling installation to prevent undue wear and tear on the nylon rope. You should install an open-end wire rope thimble between each rope clamp and the screw eye above it.

The clamps and rope are generally available at marine supply houses.

Yard light installation

■ A YARD LIGHT does many things for a home. It bids welcome. It discourages prowlers. It adds nighttime beauty to the yard, and lights the way to your front door.

The biggest job in installing a yard light is digging the hole for the post and the trench for the cable. The required minimum depth is 18 in., and you'll find a narrow spade best for digging the trench.

Yard lights come with metal or wood posts, plain or fancy. The important thing when setting the post in concrete is to see that it's plumb before filling the hole. Here, in the case of a wooden post, a couple of C-clamps can be used to attach braces to it temporarily; with a metal post, notches in the braces will let you hook them over the top.

Use heavy-duty, flat, plastic-covered cable made for underground burial and run it up inside the yard-light post, leaving ample wire at the top for connecting it later to the socket. Buy three bags of dry-mix concrete to set the post, mix according to directions and fill the hole.

To connect the cable to an existing junction box in the basement, you have to pass it through a hole in the foundation wall or a hole in the joist header. The latter is an easier job if you have a poured foundation, but it means the cable must be partially exposed. In this case, the exposed part must pass through conduit before entering the house wall.

While they cost more, you can buy yard lights that turn themselves on and off at dusk and dawn by a built-in photoelectric control. This feature eliminates the need for a separate switch. However, the drawing on the next page shows how to install a separate switch at some convenient location in the house, and the wiring diagram below shows how you connect the wires of the cables to the black and white wires you'll find in the junction box when you remove its cover. Turn off the electricity when making the connections, and remember to connect black wires to black and white wires to white.

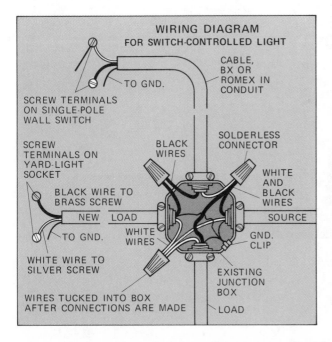

WIRING DIAGRAM
FOR SWITCH-CONTROLLED LIGHT

TO GND.
CABLE, BX OR ROMEX IN CONDUIT
SCREW TERMINALS ON SINGLE-POLE WALL SWITCH
SCREW TERMINALS ON YARD-LIGHT SOCKET
BLACK WIRES
SOLDERLESS CONNECTOR
WHITE AND BLACK WIRES
BLACK WIRE TO BRASS SCREW
NEW LOAD
SOURCE
TO GND.
WHITE WIRES
GND. CLIP
WHITE WIRE TO SILVER SCREW
EXISTING JUNCTION BOX
WIRES TUCKED INTO BOX AFTER CONNECTIONS ARE MADE
LOAD

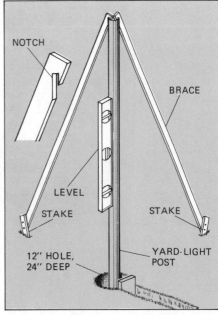

NOTCH
BRACE
LEVEL
STAKE
STAKE
12" HOLE, 24" DEEP
YARD-LIGHT POST

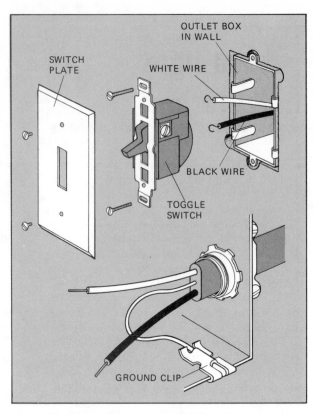

SWITCH PLATE

OUTLET BOX IN WALL

WHITE WIRE

BLACK WIRE

TOGGLE SWITCH

GROUND CLIP

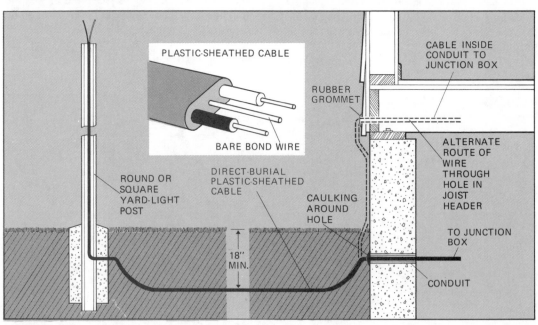

PLASTIC-SHEATHED CABLE

BARE BOND WIRE

ROUND OR SQUARE YARD-LIGHT POST

DIRECT-BURIAL PLASTIC-SHEATHED CABLE

CAULKING AROUND HOLE

RUBBER GROMMET

CABLE INSIDE CONDUIT TO JUNCTION BOX

ALTERNATE ROUTE OF WIRE THROUGH HOLE IN JOIST HEADER

TO JUNCTION BOX

CONDUIT

18" MIN.

Mercury vapor lamp uses less energy

■ TODAY, ELECTRIC POST LAMPS offer the most economical and protective illumination for your driveway, walk, steps and entrances. Thanks to a new mercury vapor bulb, you can now illu- minate the outside of your home with a brighter, longer-lasting light that uses less energy.

Compared to a typical 100-w. household-type bulb, a 50-w. mercury vapor bulb lasts 21 times as long and gives off almost twice as much light per watt. A 100-w. household bulb lasts about 750 hours (three months if lighted an average of eight hours a day), but the mercury bulb will burn about 16,000 hours (more than five years at the same daily rate).

The new elliptical mercury bulb operates on a 120-v. circuit. But since it requires a ballast, it cannot simply be screwed into a conventional light socket. Several outdoor lighting manu- facturers have designed cast-aluminum postlight fixtures for the mercury vapor bulb. They offer

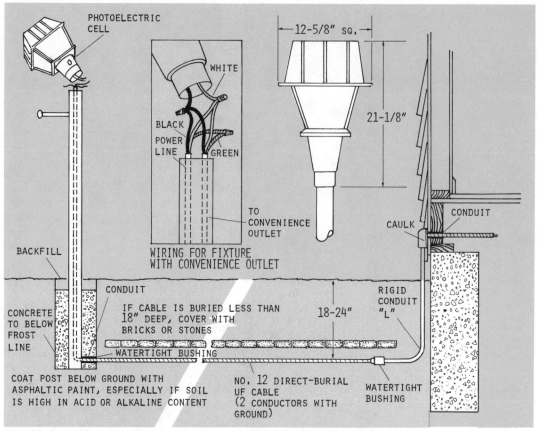

CONVERTING A standard electric post light can be as simple as removing the existing fixture head, and connecting the mercury vapor unit.

excellent light distribution from an unbreakable lens.

Before installing a new lamp, check with your local building department to assure electrical code compliance. Then dig a post hole—lower than the area frost line—and a trench to the power source, following details in the diagram above. Once the cable is laid in the trench and wired through the post, place the post in the hole, plumb and secure it in both planes with rope and stakes. Usually a 45-lb. bag of concrete mix will fill the hole to about 6 in. below ground level. Backfill the hole and trench, and replace sod. Pull a plastic bag over the post top and seal it with tape to guard against moisture. Let concrete set 24 to 48 hours, then remove the bag and mount the fixture head by wiring as follows:

To wire fixture only. Attach the black cable wire to the black fixture wire, white cable wire to the white fixture wire, and green wire to ground on cable.

To wire the outdoor, weatherproof convenience outlet to provide a plug-in receptacle at the post. Connect the black convenience-outlet (CO) wire to the black cable wire, white CO wire to white cable wire and green CO wire to ground wire on the cable.

To wire a photoelectric-cell collar to the fixture. (This device turns light on at dusk, off at dawn.) Connect the white wire from the photo cell and fixture to the white cable wire; connect the black wire from the photo cell to the black cable wire; then connect the red wire from the photo cell to the black fixture wire. Aim photo cell toward the north.

To wire a photoelectric cell, convenience outlet and fixture. Connect the white wires from the fixture, photo cell and convenience outlet (CO) to white cable wire; connect the black fixture wire to the red wire on the photo cell; connect the black wires from the photo cell and CO to black cable wire; then connect the green CO wire to ground wire on the cable. Use solderless connectors and wrap with electrical tape.

If the power source is a surface outlet on the exterior of your house, turn off the circuit and attach an L-shaped conduit to the outlet box. Pull cable wire through the conduit and connect it to corresponding color-coded wires in the outlet—white to white, black to black. If an outside outlet is not available, run conduit through the basement wall and make connections at the nearest junction box.

A metal fixture or post must be grounded. When no convenience outlet is used, run ground wire to fixture. With an outlet (which can also be wired at base of the post), ground the receptacle box to the ground post and fixture. A waterproof outlet box at the house entry should have an internal ground screw for ground-wire connection.

Converting a gas post light is easy, but the gas line should be capped by a professional gas-pipe installer.

INSTALLATION OF LAMP POST

INSTALLATION TOOLS AND MATERIALS

MATERIALS

1. No. 12 direct-burial type UF cable wire (2 conductors with ground)
2. Solderless connectors (6)
3. Plastic electrical tape
4. 45-lb. bag of dry concrete mix
5. Heavy-plastic bag (minimum 4-in. dia.)
6. Rope
7. Stakes (4)
8. L-shaped conduit
9. Conduit sleeves (2)
10. Watertight bushings (2)

TOOLS

1. Spade
2. Long-nose pliers
3. Wire stripper
4. Screwdriver

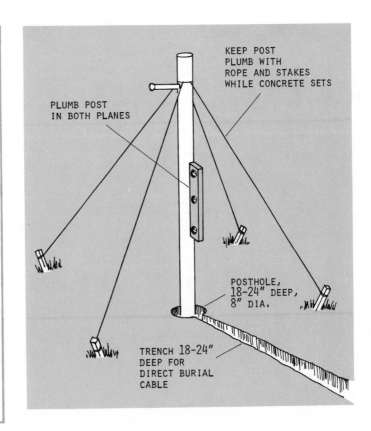

KEEP POST PLUMB WITH ROPE AND STAKES WHILE CONCRETE SETS

PLUMB POST IN BOTH PLANES

POSTHOLE, 18-24" DEEP, 8" DIA.

TRENCH 18-24" DEEP FOR DIRECT BURIAL CABLE

Shrubbery light

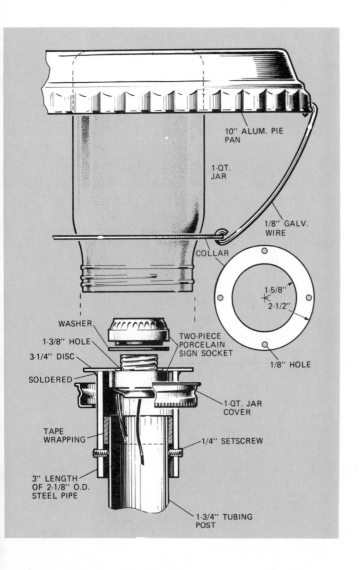

10" ALUM. PIE PAN

1-QT. JAR

1/8" GALV. WIRE

COLLAR

1-5/8"
2-1/2"

1/8" HOLE

WASHER

1-3/8" HOLE

3-1/4" DISC

SOLDERED

TWO-PIECE PORCELAIN SIGN SOCKET

1-QT. JAR COVER

TAPE WRAPPING

1/4" SETSCREW

3" LENGTH OF 2-1/8" O.D. STEEL PIPE

1-3/4" TUBING POST

■ AN ALUMINUM pie pan and a quart mayonnaise jar make an attractive shrubbery light.

The pie pan top is held in place by four wire braces and a metal collar. Cut the collar from 16-ga. sheet aluminum with a circle cutter on a drill press. Make holes 90° apart in both the collar and pie pan for ⅛-in. aluminum wire.

Replace the vacuum-seal jar cover with a metal disc made from a round outlet-box cover with a knockout hole in the center. Enlarge the knockout to accept a standard porcelain sign socket and solder the disc to a short piece of galvanized pipe. The disc and jar cover provide a watertight seal. Three setscrews hold the light to its 1¾-in. o.d. post. Friction tape around the top of the 30-in.-long post builds up its o.d. so it fits snugly inside the larger pipe. Use a 40-w. bulb.

For a yard light, attach the light to a 5-ft. post. In all cases, set the post in concrete and bring up ample wire inside the pipe to connect the socket. Run heavy-duty, direct-burial cable underground and wire the light to an inside switch.

Pottery anyone can make

■ THE SIMPLE METHOD used to make this decorative pot is one you can learn in an afternoon: On various textured fabrics you roll clay into slabs, cut them to shape and combine the pieces.

The clay should be moist as you work. Knead it until smooth and free of air bubbles when cut in half. Smooth seams with a moist sponge. Each time you seam pieces together, set the work aside for an hour or two until the clay stiffens slightly but is still moist enough to seam with the next section. Cover the completed piece with a plastic bag several days so it dries slowly. Remove the bag and air the clay several more days until it's dry to the touch, then fire it.

When you fire the kiln, rest it on fireproof bricks or concrete floor. After firing, *don't open kiln until it is cool* (at least six hours with the kiln shown). The pot needs two firings in the kiln shown—a bisque firing for 1½ to 2 hours at about 1873° and a glaze firing of 2½ to 3 hours at 2174°.

Gradually cover the kiln as it heats. This may take 45 minutes. The correct firing temperature is reached when a 1-in.-high cone, placed on a pad of clay inside the kiln, droops over. Use a No. 06 cone for bisque firing and a No. 6 for glaze firing. A melting cone is a sign to turn off the heat and cool.

After bisque firing, sponge on a red iron oxide wash (one rounded teaspoon to one cup water) to darken the recessed area. Rub it off after two minutes. Pour a coat of glaze in the pot to waterproof it; glaze-fire.

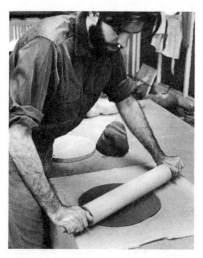

1. This pot is an excellent first project. Roll clay to a ¼-in.-thick slab somewhat like rolling pie crust.

2. Use any round object with a 6½-in. diameter as a template to cut a circle for bottom of the pot.

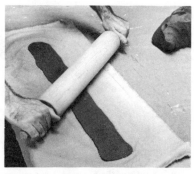

3. Hand shape a 1½-in.-dia. clay coil. Sprinkle grog (or sand) on canvas to give the clay texture and roll it flat.

4. Trim the slab edges straight to a 2½-in. width. This slab wraps around pot bottom to begin forming sides.

5. Score the edge of the bottom with a fork to aid adherence. As you work, score all points where slabs meet.

6. Also aid adherence by brushing pure vinegar on all seam edges. Wrap slab around pot bottom, overlap ends, seam.

7. After seams are pinched together, press a decorative clay button on the side seam. Let dry an hour or two.

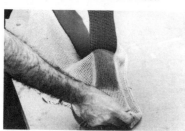

8. Shape a ¾-in.-diameter coil, roll it on a fabric to get texture, and peel it off. Trim to 1¼-in. width.

9. Score pot at seam, brush vinegar on all seam edges. Wrap slab around pot bottom, overlap ends, seam.

10. After rolling top slab on fabric for texture, peel off slab. Place pot upside down on slab; cut top.

11. After top of pot is treated and seamed, cut top opening using a 3½-in.-dia. template; let pot dry.

12. Roll a ½-in.-dia. clay coil to use as the neck of the pot. Flatten it, then trim to 1-in. width and attach.

13. Use a pin tool to prick decorative holes in pot neck. Then flatten pencil-sized coil around neck seam.

14. Shape two ⅜ x 1 x 3-in. handle supports. Cut handle holes. Score, apply vinegar and attach supports.

15. Roll handle coil, place it through the support holes and add a pea-sized handle stop near each end.

16. Place dry pot and a cone in kiln. Be sure cone is visible in kiln window.

MATERIALS AND TOOLS LIST

3 lbs. moist, de-aired stoneware clay (clay with air pockets can explode in the kiln).

Vinegar (to help pieces adhere).

Red iron oxide colorant; pin tool to cut clay.

Commercially prepared glaze, compatible with firing temperature of clay, to waterproof pot.

Grog (fired and ground clay) or sand for texture.

Rolling pin, textured fabrics, fork (to score clay).

Workboard (to turn piece when it's wet).

Small paintbrush (to apply vinegar).

6½-in.-dia. and 3½-in.-dia. templates to use as cutting guides; e.g., pail or jar.

Small kiln with firing cones.

EACH CLAY SAMPLE was rolled on the fabric behind it to acquire a texture. Experiment with materials—try grasses and leaves—to get desirable, complementing patterns.

Potter's wheel you can make

■ LIKE A FOREIGN LANGUAGE, such terms as "kicking," "wedging," "necking" and "throwing" are Greek to one who has yet to experience the fun of forming a hunk of clay into an attractive vase on a potter's wheel. But they soon become common parlance, and you'll know

TOOLS YOU'LL NEED

A Plaster bats	**D** Paring/potter's knife	**G** Natural and
B Calipers	**E** Pointer	elephant-ear sponges
C Lifters	**F** Cutting wire	**H** Foot rimmers

I Sponge on stick
J Level
K Wooden ribs

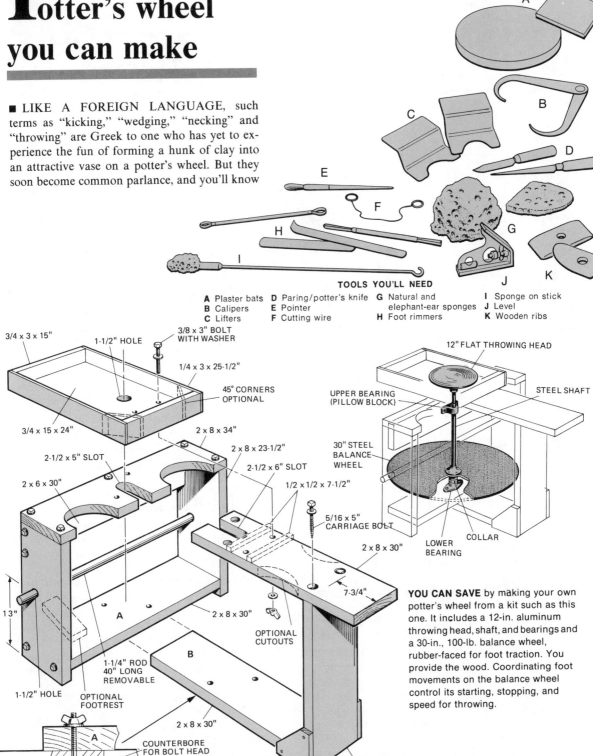

YOU CAN SAVE by making your own potter's wheel from a kit such as this one. It includes a 12-in. aluminum throwing head, shaft, and bearings and a 30-in., 100-lb. balance wheel, rubber-faced for foot traction. You provide the wood. Coordinating foot movements on the balance wheel control its starting, stopping, and speed for throwing.

1. WEDGE clay to remove air bubbles and form two or three softball-size lumps. Then slam one lump on the center of the wheel head or on a moistened bat to make it stick firmly in place.

2. SET wheel in motion by kicking it forward with the right foot. When it spins remove the foot and begin working the clay ball with hands to the center of the wheel. Don't kick and shape at the same time.

3. WHEN clay is centered, open it with the thumbs, working them down slowly to about ¼ in. from the base. Steady hand control is important; brace your right elbow against your side to help.

HOW TO WEDGE CLAY

Your clay is made workable by a process called wedging. Similar to kneading dough, wedging is done before the clay is placed on the potter's wheel, a necessary step to remove air bubbles and pockets from the clay.

First your clay lump is cut in half. Then one half of it is slammed down on top of the other, with cut side out. This step is repeated many times until the pockets of air are forced from the clay, and finally the well-wedged lump is shaped into a four-sided loaf by patting the ends with the hands.

Wedging the clay is a most important step, not only in removing air bubbles but in producing uniformity of texture in the clay.

7. AS NEEDED, trim the uneven top with a pin tool to keep the clay balanced so the cylinder stays centered. Trim enough from the top so no segment is carrying an extra mass that could disturb balance.

8. CONTINUING upward pulls produce a larger cylinder with a thinner wall. As the wall thins, slow the kick-wheel speed. If the work collapses, you'll have to remove the clay and start over.

that necking in pottery means shaping the neck of a pot. The best way to get started in pottery is to take lessons. The beginner can read how it's done and learn the fundamentals, but there's nothing like watching a skilled potter pull up a pot from a mass of spinning clay on a potter's wheel to really see how it's done. Even then, the beginner is not going to "throw" a perfect pot the very first try. Like all hobbies, it takes practice.

After the pot has been shaped, trimmed and dried, finishing it requires materials and equipment difficult for beginning potters to assemble on their own. This is another good reason for the novice to link up with a studio. The place where you take lessons will usually let you glaze and fire your pieces for a fee even after the course is over. First the dried piece, known as green ware, is fired in a kiln, either gas or electric, until the clay takes on the characteristics of an ordinary flowerpot. It is now known as bisque and is ready for glazing. Some studios use ready-mixed glazes and some mix their own and store them in big crocks in which the pots can be dipped. After the piece is glazed, it is fired again at a very high temperature. Stoneware pottery is fired to 2350°F. in a gas kiln. This final firing produces a glasslike surface and makes the pot durable.

The main costs of starting in pottery are the purchase of a wheel or a kit to build one and the initial lessons. However, clay is cheap—about 12 cents a pound for stoneware clay—and the tools needed by a beginner are simple and often can be found in your own home.

Start with a knife and fork from your kitchen, and a sponge (used to wet the clay while throwing) from the cosmetics section of a drugstore. Cut off the corner of an old chamois to smooth the rim of the pot after throwing it. A thin but strong piece of wire in the toolbox is used to cut the pot off the wheel head. You do have to buy trimming tools to finish the bottoms of your pieces after they become partially dry—"leather-hard" is the term potters use. These tools are available at most art supply stores.

4. START FORMING your cylinder by pulling the clay upward with your thumbs. Use little pressure with the hands. Each upward pull will gradually thin the clay wall and make the cylinder taller.

5. FOR BETTER control, join your hands whenever possible, locking the thumbs together or resting the left thumb on the right hand. Place and remove your hands slowly so you don't move the clay.

6. CYLINDERS tend to flare out at the top; they must be closed in by necking. Cup your hands around the cylinder center—a maneuver that makes the wall thicken and, gradually, rise straight.

9. USE A taut wire to cut work free of the wheel head after trimming excess clay from the base with a wooden tool. Put the wire under the base and pull. If the work is on a bat, just lift it from the wheel.

10. IF NO BAT was used and the work thrown on the wheel head itself, slide the work gently, after cutting it free, onto a board or plaster bat and let it dry until it's ready for glazing and firing.

RECOMMENDED BOOKS

There are many books that are helpful to the beginning potter. Here are two suggestions:

The Complete Book of Pottery Making by John B. Kenny, Chilton Book Co., Philadelphia, publisher;

Throwing on the Potter's Wheel by Thomas Sellers. Professional Publications, Columbus, Ohio, publisher;

For the more advanced potter:
Pottery, the Technique of Throwing by John Colbeck. Watson-Guptill, Inc., New York, N.Y., publisher;

Clay and Glazes for the Potter by Daniel Rhodes. Chilton Book Co., Philadelphia, Pa., publisher;

Step by Step Ceramics by Jolyon Hofsted. Golden Press, Inc., New York, N.Y.;

Later on, make some plaster bats—solid, dish-shaped slabs that you attach to the wheel head when throwing a pot and remove to let the pot dry. The plaster for making bats can be purchased from a hardware store, and pie plates make good molds.

Firing charges can be rather high, especially if you make big pieces. The rate might be higher in a commercial art center than at an adult education center. This fee covers the cost of both firings and the use of the glazes. When you are more experienced, you can cut these costs by purchasing your own kiln and mixing or buying your own glazes. Although some people feel the gas kiln produces a more beautiful and subtle glaze, many find the electric kiln, with its more evenly distributed heat, provides more predictable results.

For the beginner, however, developing skill on the wheel will be the primary concern. The accompanying pictures demonstrate the steps in forming the basic cylinder from which most shapes are made. It is useful to have such pictures to refer back to again and again as you work. But pictures and books can only go so far and a complete beginner will find it hard to learn without some instruction from a teacher.

For instance, the very first step in making a pot—kneading, cutting and pounding the clay to eliminate air bubbles and produce a uniform texture—is hard to pick up on your own. "Wedging," as the process is called, is most easily understood by watching a demonstration. Later, when your pot disintegrates in a soggy pile on the wheel head for the fifth time in a row, perhaps the teacher can tell you the one small thing you were doing wrong so that it won't happen again. It will be a while before the pot you see in your mind will be the one you end up with. But in time it will come and you will get great satisfaction from turning out handsome and useful things on your potter's wheel.

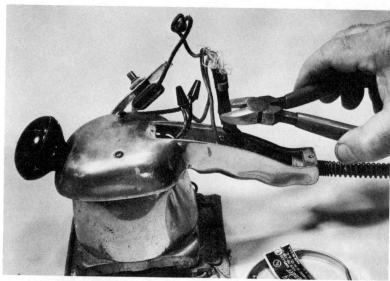

1 TO REPLACE a frayed cord that enters a tool through the handle, clip it off near end, but leave connections intact for future reference.

2 MAKE A SLIT in new cord's cover and bare enough wire to make connection. Trim off excess with scissors.

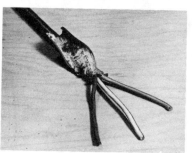

3 NOTE WIRE colors in new cord. Connect wires to motor leads and ground; use originals as guide.

4 USE SCREW-ON connectors or pigtails and tape insulation when rewiring. Fold wires into handle.

5 USE THREE-PRONG plug with new three-wire cord to help assure grounding. Screw clamp grips the cord.

Power tool tuneup

■ THE BEST GUIDE to maintaining any power tool is the owner's manual. Keep yours filed in a safe place and, if you lose it, send to the manufacturer for another. Specify the age, model number and any other descriptive information you can find on the tool.

If your tool is an orphan for which needed replacement parts aren't available from the original source, look in a classified telephone directory for suppliers of the same type of item. You can often

VACUUM-CLEANER snorkel made from soft copper tube flattened at end can clear dust from tight spots.

TO INSPECT toothed belt, put white card behind it and turn sprocket. Look for frayed edges and ripped teeth.

CLEAN slide ways and toolpost mount of compound rest with stiff brush. Lubricate ways whenever lathe is used.

BRUSHING with toothbrush cleans metal chips from feed-screw threads. Turn screw holding brush to threads.

OLD TOWEL spread on bench when you open power tools keeps small parts from rolling away (above, right). Observe how parts go together and watch for springs that may pop out. Clean commutator (shown at card corner in photo above, left) with fine aluminum-oxide abrasive. Hold abrasive to commutator; turn fan; blow to clean off dirt particles. Ring connector fits top of holder to supply current (left).

match bearings, motor brushes, drive belts and other parts.

Lubrication rules of thumb

Locate all oil holes and occasionally feed them a few drops of light oil like household oil or No. 20 engine oil. Self-lubricating graphited sleeve bearings need oil too, and many have oil holes. If not, put a few drops on the shaft at the end of the sleeve so it can work in; wipe off excess. Do not oil sealed-for-life, grease-packed ball bearings. The oil may leach out of the grease and wreck the bearing. Finally, don't overlubricate; oil may seep out and form a sticky mass of oil and dirt that gums up the works.

Stationary power tools

● **Table saws:** If you've neglected a table saw or any other tool with a cast-iron table, its ground surface may have rusted—especially in a garage workshop. Remove rust from the surface and grooves with a rust remover. Wear gloves and goggles and follow the directions on the label. For added luster, rub the surface with 220-grit aluminum oxide paper. (In woodworking, rust removal is essential to keep rust from transferring to the work, which may cause finishing problems.) Protect the restored table with an oil film or rust-preventive lubricant.

To check your table saw's tilt control, first thoroughly vacuum-clean the unit. Set the control at zero, raise the blade to maximum height and place a try square on the table against the blade. If the blade isn't square with the table, adjust the stop under the table.

Keep your saw's motor clean since sawdust can foul the centrifugal switch that changes over from starter winding to running winding. If it

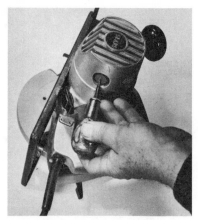

BRUSHES can be checked and changed in some tools like this Sears circular saw without opening motor housing.

MARK BRUSH and spring clip with penciled X on one side so both can be replaced in original positions. Mark will shine on brush.

INTERVALS between regreasing gears of circular saws and sabre saws vary with model, but range from 100 to 200 hours of operation.

CLEAN SAWDUST from table saw with vacuum. Dirt can pack against stops and affect cutting accuracy.

SWING COVER plate clear to get at wick-packed opening for lubrication of shaft bearing on some saw models (left). Saturate wick, but don't over-oil. Reduce dust in motor with cardboard panel cut to fit around belt (shown above) and second panel with vent holes to cover front (not shown in photo).

USE LIGHT oil to wipe protective film onto drill-press column; use gear grease on the feed-lever mechanism.

CLEAN RUST from tables and lathe ways with rust remover. Right side of this table has been restored.

USE TOOTHPICK to remove dust blockage from clogged oil holes. Work carefully so you don't push in dirt.

BANDSAW blade should be centered on tire, using wheel-tilting adjustment. Cover has been removed for photo.

sticks in the starter position, it can burn out the winding. If it sticks in the running position, the motor won't start.

Check belt drive tension. You should be able to push the belt inward ½ in. on short spans and about 1 in. on longer ones. Minor slippage can be cured with a belt dressing. An overtight belt doesn't last long and increases bearing wear.

Be sure the blade is sharp. A dull one increases bearing and belt wear because of the heavier load and longer running time. It also increases the chance of the work being kicked back at you, so consider a sharp blade a primary safety factor in operating your saw.

● **Radial-arm saw:** To cure out-of-square end cuts, use a try square to check squareness with the table. The means of adjustment varies, but is likely to be two bolts at the side of the bevel latch. Loosened, they permit tilting the motor until the blade is exactly flush with the square. Tightened, they hold it that way.

Saw travel should also be squared with the guide fence. Make a trial cut through a wide board with a dressed edge against the fence and check it with a carpenter's square. If it's out of square, the saw track isn't perpendicular to the fence. To realign, first loosen the track arm clamp handle and lay a steel square on the table with one edge against the fence. Then pull the saw carriage slowly across the table to see how much and which way the travel is untrue.

The adjustment is usually on the miter latch, often a hex nut and setscrew or cap nut. Try adjustments carefully. The hex nut may automatically swing the track arm left or right, depending on the way it's turned. When you're satisfied, tighten the setscrew or cap nut to hold the new setting. There are also other adjusting arrangements; read your manual carefully.

Saw "heeling" may occur even when the track arm is square with the fence. This means that the teeth at the back of the blade are not following the kerf made by the teeth at the front. You feel a drag when you make a cut. Check it by making a cut into a board, but without pulling it past the board. If the saw is heeling, you'll see tooth (heel) marks at one end. Viewed from the front, heel

WELL MAINTAINED 40-year-old lathe and motor are in fine shape. Weight of motor on hinged platform tensions belt to overhead jackshaft. Belt from jackshaft to lathe is tensioned by adjusting screw to reduce drive-belt load on the lathe's bearings.

HINGED jackshaft platform (far left) is adjusted by tightening or loosening nuts on either end of ½-in.-dia. threaded rod. Make a cover (near left) to protect oil holes close to sources of sawdust or metal particles. Snap-on sheet-metal cover (shown in hand) is used over lathe headstock bearing. Cover lathe bed ways when grinding.

marks on the right mean the back of the blade should be shifted to the left. Marks on the left call for shifting the rear of the blade to the right.

To adjust for heeling, loosen yoke clamp handle and swivel adjustment bolts. The lock bolts are often under a cover plate near the swivel latch. Turn the yoke as required, tightening and testing, until the heel marks vanish. Then tighten the yoke clamp handle, followed by the bolts. On some saw models, heel-correcting adjustments are at the yoke's motor-pivot point.

● **Drill press:** Since most drill-press motors in recent years have sealed bearings, only quill and feed lever mechanisms are likely to need oiling. If there's play in the quill from wear (not likely with average use), look for a wear adjustment bolt. Some drill presses have it. Check the drive belt for correct tension as described for table saws. The tension can be adjusted by moving the motor and retightening the mounting bolts.

● **Bandsaw:** Check your saw adjustments starting with the blade by opening the upper wheel guard. If the blade is not centered on the wheel tire, use the tilting adjustment to tilt the wheel in or out until it is. Test by turning the wheel by hand with the drive pulley removed. Next adjust the blade tension. If your saw has no tension scale, adjust the tension handle at the top until the blade allows a side flex of ¼ in. on a 6-in. span between upper and lower guides. Set the upper guide far enough above the table to provide the span.

Prior to tensioning, be sure you have proper clearance between the blade and the guide pins in the upper and lower guide assemblies. For most blades, the distance between the guide pins and the blade is .002 to .003 in. Refer to your manual. You can get this clearance by placing pieces of medium-weight paper between the loosened pins and the sides of the blade, then tightening the pins in place against the paper. When the paper is pulled out, the proper clearance remains. Be sure upper and lower pins are in line so the blade isn't pushed out of vertical. Pins should be adjusted to come just behind the blade teeth. If they touch the teeth, they'll dull the blade. If they're too far back, they won't be able to guide the blade adequately.

The blade support (ball-bearing wheel behind the blade) should be set ¼₄ in. from the back edge of the blade. If it runs in constant contact with the blade, it may cause case hardening and eventual blade breakage. With proper clearance, it runs in contact only when work is pushed through the saw. Tires on bandsaw wheels last almost indefinitely as long as you keep them clean. If they're scored slightly from long use, dress them down a little with coarse sandpaper, but be careful not to remove too much surface from the tire.

● **Lathe:** The wood lathe is equipped with heavy-duty headstock bearings because of the loads imposed. They may be roller, sleeve, or cone types requiring lubrication, or sealed "lifetime" ball types that require no additional lubrication.

The lathe bed ways (smooth-ground upper surfaces) and those of the compound rest (if the lathe has one) all require an oil coating for rust prevention and for lubrication since they are precision parts. Feed screws in the compound rest and tailstock also require oiling. For best maintenance and tension, see suggestions given earlier for belt-driven tools.

Check the bed with a level at both ends. If any twist in the bed is indicated, use shims under the mountings to correct it.

Portable power tools

● **Power drills:** Most power drills are easy to service. In "clamshell" form, the drill housing separates in two halves when assembly screws are removed. All internal parts are then exposed, including the grease in the gear case. The grease should be replaced after 100 to 200 hours of operation, or by a rule of thumb that calls for grease replacement after the second or third change of motor brushes. Scoop out most of the old grease with a screwdriver and wipe out the rest. The amount that comes out is a guide as to how much new grease you should put in, plus a little extra for the wiping cloth.

Use oil on the chuck shaft and in the rear motor bearing hole. The grease should be a tool type, formulated with enough viscosity not to work from the gear case into the motor. Makers of power tools offer such lubricants. They're sold in tubes and have a consistency like soft margarine. If the tool has a worm-gear drive, be sure the grease is suitable. Some companies make a special worm-gear grease. Don't use a free-flowing type like outboard motor lubricant.

On most tool motors, brushes should be replaced before they wear down to ³⁄₁₆ in. in length. Any shorter, and the brushes may jam and break. They're easy to get at on most portable tools. In clamshell drills, they're in removable brush holders on opposite sides of the commutator. Change them in pairs, but take them out and replace them one at a time so the brush still in place serves as a guide for replacing the other. If you can't match a set of brushes for an orphan tool, you can flat-sand a larger size down to fit.

On some drills, brushes are accessible from the outside by removing plastic caps on each side of the motor housing. On others, you remove a few screws to take off the back of the handle or a section of it to expose the brushes.

● **Sabre saw:** Sabre-saw brush replacements (usually from outside the housing) and lubrication are much the same as for drills.

To get to the grease, remove the plunger housing at the front of the saw. This may also require removal of the tool handle. Before the plunger is moved out of position, note how the crank mechanism engages the plunger so you can fit the parts back together after the grease job. The typical amount of new grease you'll need is two tablespoons.

Don't force parts together when reassembling the saw. *If you do it correctly, no force is needed.* Use oil in the oil hole for the rear motor bearing. Also oil the felt seal (if present) at the bottom of the plunger housing.

● **Portable circular saw:** Lubrication varies with the make and model, but most require occasional light oiling of the rear motor bearing through an oil hole.

To give your portable circular saw a grease job, first disconnect it from the power source and remove the blade. Next, unscrew the upper guard cover and disconnect the retracting spring of the lower (swinging) guard. Remove the dust cover that closes the side of the upper guard to expose the gear housing. Unscrew the gear housing cover screws and pry off gear housing cover to get at the old grease. Renew the grease following steps described for power drills. The typical amount in a 7-in. Stanley saw is ½ oz.

You can thoroughly clean the gear housing with kerosene if you're careful not to let it enter the sleeve bearings. Then reassemble the saw by reversing the order of part removal.

Brushes on portable circular saws are usually accessible from outside the motor housing.

Clogged vent holes can cause overheating. Keep them free of sawdust accumulations.

● **Router:** This is one of the simplest tools to maintain. Many have sealed ball bearings that require no further lubrication. If yours has oil holes, use a few drops of light oil in them at intervals. And check the collet that holds the bits just in case it is starting to show signs of wear. One important servicing measure: Use an air hose or pump to blow out any sawdust or chips that may have lodged in the motor.

● **Sanders:** The attention a sander needs depends to some extent on when it was made. Many recent models require no lubrication as all bearings are sealed and permanently lubricated. Some older ones with self-lubricating bearings are much the same. The orbital model shown in the cord replacement photo has been regularly used for 25 years without lubrication. Your best bet, lacking the service manual, is to look for oil holes or fittings and oil them lightly. If brushings are visible and the tool has been in use for considerable time, light oiling is helpful.

It's wise to blow or vacuum sawdust accumulations out of the tool frequently. Check the brushes at intervals, replace them if necessary.

WEAR SAFETY GOGGLES

Stands for your power tools

■ EACH OF THESE TOOL STANDS was made of sheathing-grade plywood, which is a couple dollars cheaper per sheet than A-D plywood. The rough surface of the sheathing makes little difference, but if you like things a little smoother, use A-D plywood.

To capitalize on the 4 x 8-ft. sheet, dimensions are kept at 12, 16, 24 and 32 in. when possible. Actually these dimensions are minus half the width of a saw kerf so that a sheet will cut up, for instance, into three pieces a shy 16 in. wide.

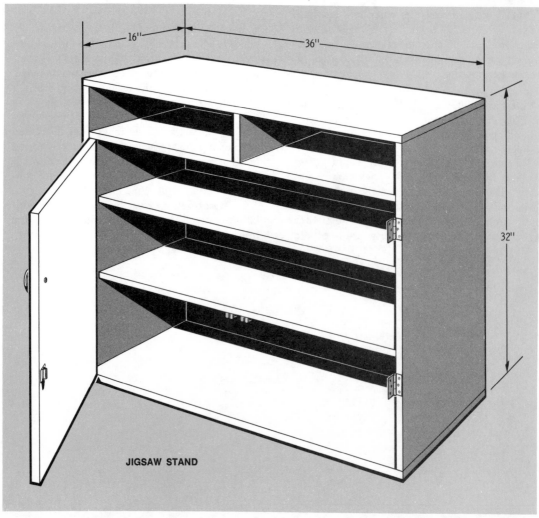

JIGSAW STAND

Nails and glue are used throughout, except for fastening the drawer dividers and glides to the sidewalls of the drill-press unit. These are screwed and glued. Since there is a back (or a divider as in the case of the bandsaw base) to prevent the unit from racking, nail-and-glue assembly is sufficiently strong. Quarter-inch plywood or ⅛-in. hardboard work best for cabinet backs, drawer bottoms and dividers.

You'll thank yourself for going whole hog on the casters. If they are big enough (2-in. wheels) and well made, you'll roll tools around a concrete floor with ease. Cheap, small casters roll poorly and are blocked by the smallest sliver on the floor.

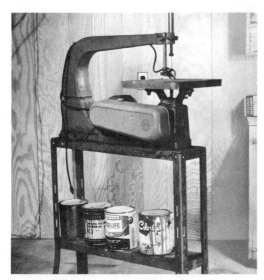

JIG SAW STAND (left) lets you use the valuable space going to waste under your power tool.

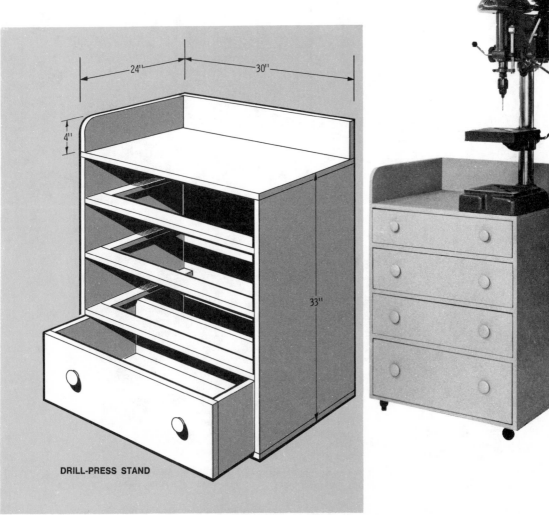

DRILL-PRESS STAND

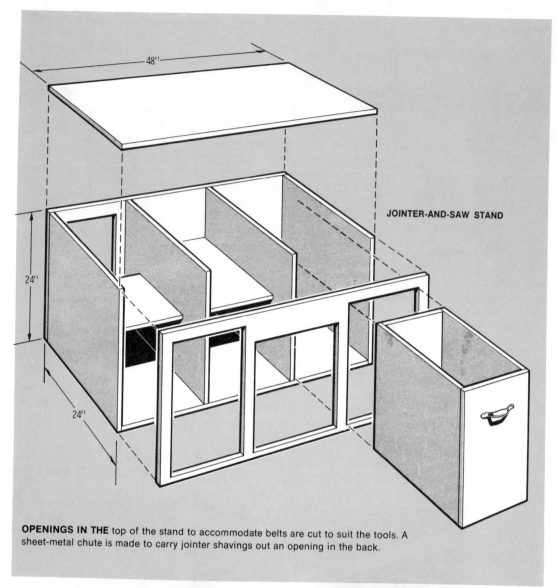

JOINTER-AND-SAW STAND

48"

24"

24"

OPENINGS IN THE top of the stand to accommodate belts are cut to suit the tools. A sheet-metal chute is made to carry jointer shavings out an opening in the back.

YOUR SAW AND jointer should be side by side on a single stand. This one has storage, a sawdust bin, and a jointer chute.

JOINTER MOTOR on a hinged shelf adjusts the belt tension.

The drill-press base is largely a "set" design for its use and its shape. You need a work surface beside a drill press for handy handling of the materials you use. The front-to-back depth (24 in.) makes it the best of the four stands for drawers. The other three, however, can be adapted or intermixed to suit your requirements.

For instance, the open shelves of the jigsaw stand would be just as useful under the bandsaw. Or, let's say you don't want to bother with cabinet doors. Then you install plain shelf units in all the bases. As another variation, you can put doors on one side of the double-faced shelf design under the bandsaw to provide storage for things you want to shelter from workshop dust and dirt.

Got a lathe? A perfect stand for it would be a three-section modification of the jigsaw stand. Make it 5 ft. long (20 in. to a section) and the open shelves will be perfect for lathe tools. You can get at them, but they are protected from burial under lathe shavings.

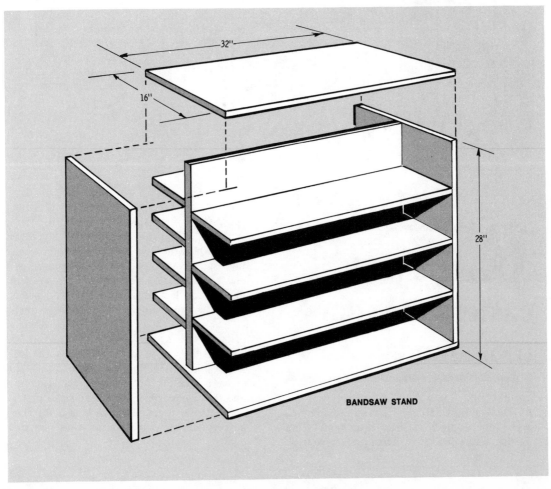

BANDSAW STAND

CASTER EXTENDED

CASTER RETRACTED

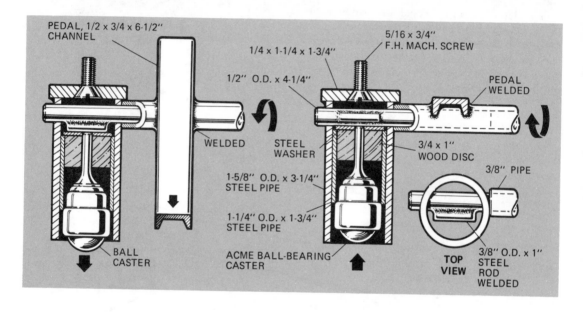

PEDAL, 1/2 x 3/4 x 6-1/2"
CHANNEL

1/4 x 1-1/4 x 1-3/4"

5/16 x 3/4"
F.H. MACH. SCREW

1/2" O.D. x 4-1/4"

PEDAL
WELDED

WELDED

STEEL
WASHER

3/4 x 1"
WOOD DISC

3/8" PIPE

1-5/8" O.D. x 3-1/4"
STEEL PIPE

1-1/4" O.D. x 1-3/4"
STEEL PIPE

BALL
CASTER

ACME BALL-BEARING
CASTER

TOP
VIEW

3/8" O.D. x 1"
STEEL
ROD
WELDED

Retractable casters for your tool stands

■ TIRED OF PUSHING, shoving and groaning every time a piece of shop equipment needs moving across the room? Then picture yourself depressing a foot pedal and rolling the tool effortlessly. By making the retractable-type caster set shown in the drawings above, you can enjoy such shop convenience. When the lever is depressed, the ball casters are forced out of their sockets and locked in a ready-to-roll position. This retractable caster is easy to make—there is no machining called for, yet it's quick-acting and positive. And, as shown in the photos, one pedal activates the pair of casters. Basically, the idea is simply a fit of 1-in. pipe into 1¼-in. pipe, and the use of a 1-in.-dia. ball caster which seats neatly into the smaller pipe. While one set of casters is adequate for a radial or table saw, it's best to have a caster on each leg of the stand to save your back.

Roll-away stand holds router and drill

■ DESIGNED SO YOU can wheel it about like a hand truck, this compact tool cabinet provides a dandy place to mount a portable-drill stand and a portable router table. What's more, there is an open shelf below where you can store a sabre saw, circular saw and finishing sander. For the man whose "workshop" consists mainly of portable electric tools, you won't find a handier setup anywhere.

Bolted to a shelf, the router table retracts into the cabinet when the shelf and supporting leg are swung upward, and a built-in sheet-metal chute funnels wood chips from the router to a catch

THE WHEELS on the rear legs of the unit let you roll this mini-workshop to the job or stow it away in a corner when you want it out of the way. It's just the thing for a handyman with limited space.

STEEL ROUTER table, bolted to a hinged shelf, converts router into a handy shaper. The table retracts and stores in the cabinet when you use drill.

box at the rear. With the base of the drill stand anchored below the cabinet's top, the latter offers a king-size drill-press "table."

The cabinet can be made of fir plywood or ¾-in. particleboard. Both ends of the cabinet are alike and are nailed to a 20x34¼-in. back, an 11x20-in. bottom shelf and a 1x2 top rail 20 in. long. A second cross rail 20 in. down from the top supports the sheet-metal chute at the front. The 4-in. wheels and supporting ⅜-in. axle must be in place, of course, as side members are glued and nailed.

The supporting leg for the router-table shelf is hinged to a 1x1 cleat glued and screwed to the front face of the shelf, then the shelf itself is hinged to the top edge of the 1x2 cross rail.

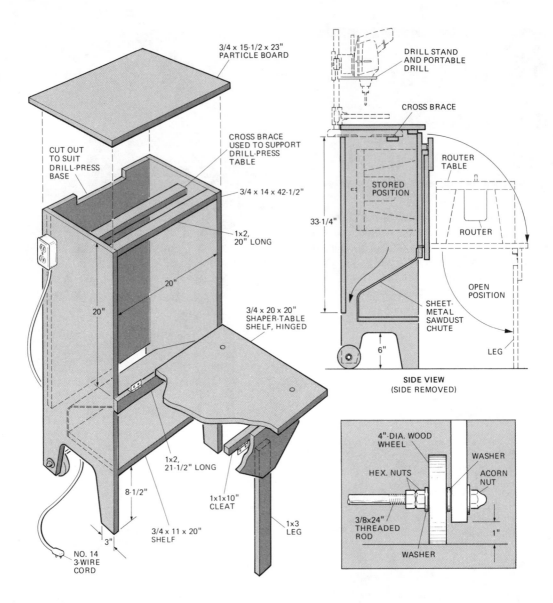

3/4 x 15-1/2 x 23"
PARTICLE BOARD

CUT OUT
TO SUIT
DRILL-PRESS
BASE

CROSS BRACE
USED TO SUPPORT
DRILL-PRESS
TABLE

3/4 x 14 x 42-1/2"

1x2,
20" LONG

20"

20"

3/4 x 20 x 20"
SHAPER-TABLE
SHELF, HINGED

1x2,
21-1/2" LONG

8-1/2"

1x1x10"
CLEAT

3"

3/4 x 11 x 20"
SHELF

1x3
LEG

NO. 14
3-WIRE
CORD

DRILL STAND
AND PORTABLE
DRILL

CROSS BRACE

ROUTER
TABLE

STORED
POSITION

ROUTER

33-1/4"

SHEET-
METAL
SAWDUST
CHUTE

OPEN
POSITION

LEG

6"

SIDE VIEW
(SIDE REMOVED)

4"-DIA. WOOD
WHEEL

WASHER

ACORN
NUT

HEX. NUTS

3/8x24"
THREADED
ROD

1"

WASHER

The side-view drawing shows how the base of
the drill-press stand rests in a notch cut in the
back panel and is bolted to a cross brace installed
between the end members of the cabinet. A
surface-mounted duplex receptacle on one side
of the cabinet fitted with a 6-ft. cord provides a
plug.

Abrasive cutoff machine you can make

■ CUTTING THROUGH 1-in. steel rod by hand is one of the most time-consuming, arm-wearying chores you can tackle in the shop. The handy little machine shown here eases the task. You get a remarkably fast and accurate cut and a surface-grinder finish on the metal.

Spare parts lying around your shop can be used to build this machine. The only tools needed are a screwdriver, wrench, hacksaw, drill press (or portable electric drill) and a ½-20 NF (national fine) die.

Basically, the machine consists of a base, riser channel, angle brackets, rocker-base pivot assembly, combination depth-of-cut adjustment and handle and the belt guard cover.

Start construction with the machine base and the rocker base. Lay out all holes as shown in the drawing on the next page and doublecheck the pillow-block dimensions (distance between mounting holes), for these may vary from those in the drawing; just allow for any difference before you drill the holes. The ⅛-in. holes are for a tension spring needed to prevent the abrasive cutting wheel from being forced into the work-piece by gravity.

When drilling the rocker base, make certain the countersink is deep enough for the two ⅜-16 NC (national coarse) fh slotted machine bolts to lie flush within the plate surface. Make an error

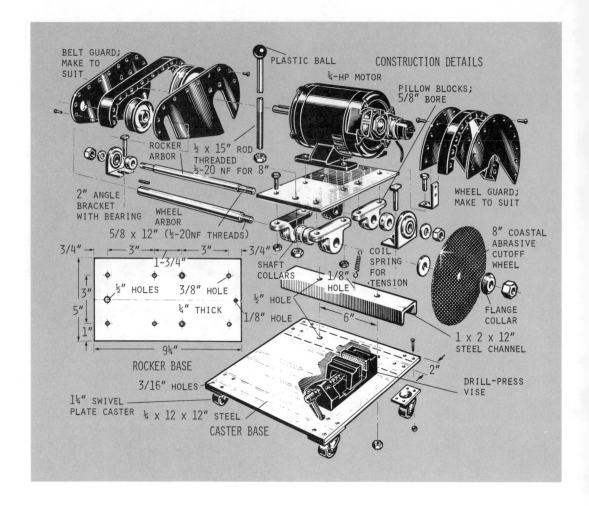

BELT GUARD; MAKE TO SUIT

PLASTIC BALL

CONSTRUCTION DETAILS

¼-HP MOTOR

PILLOW BLOCKS; 5/8" BORE

ROCKER ARBOR

½ x 15" ROD THREADED ½-20 NF FOR 8"

WHEEL GUARD; MAKE TO SUIT

2" ANGLE BRACKET WITH BEARING

WHEEL ARBOR

5/8 x 12" (½-20NF THREADS)

8" COASTAL ABRASIVE CUTOFF WHEEL

SHAFT COLLARS

COIL SPRING FOR TENSION

FLANGE COLLAR

3/4" — 3" — 3" — 3/4"

1-3/4"

3" ½" HOLES   3/8" HOLE

5" ¼" THICK

1"

9¼"

ROCKER BASE

3/16" HOLES

1¼" SWIVEL PLATE CASTER

½" HOLE

1/8" HOLE

1/8" HOLE

6"

1 x 2 x 12" STEEL CHANNEL

DRILL-PRESS VISE

¼ x 12 x 12" STEEL

CASTER BASE

here and there's a good chance the motor's base might twist and break its weld from the motor when you're tightening it in place.

The combination depth-of-cut adjustment and handle regulates how far you can lower the cutting wheel, also keeps the wheel from cutting into the base. It also serves as the handle.

The belt guard cover, used for safety as well as looks, can be made of sheet metal; use Pop rivets to hold it together.

After making all parts except the belt guard cover, start assembly with the rocker base, regarding the end with the ½-in. drilled hole as the front. After the unit is assembled—mostly a matter of patience and trial-and-error fitting—install the power cord and mount the switch.

All shafts and pillow blocks can be obtained from local hardware stores. They come as a set for use as mandrels for buffing and the like. One shaft (for the rocker) from these sets should have a ⅝-in.-dia. bearing surface with both ends turned down to ½-in. diameter with ½-20 NF thread.

Attach any special wheel with large washers on both sides and secure it with a ½-20 NF hex head machine nut.

Adjust belt tension by sliding the motor back and forth. Don't make the belt too tight; pressed at the center, it should deflect about ½ in.

The machine throws a lot of sparks, so always put on safety goggles before you use it. A common drill-press vise is used to hold the work.

THE SAW BEING USED (above) to cut ½-in. steel rod. The side shield has been removed to show the cutting operation. In actual use, the side shield should always be fastened in place to protect the operator.

A REAR VIEW of the cutoff machine (left) shows how the portable saw is attached to the vertical supports. Since it isn't convenient to control the saw with its own in-handle switch, the switch is taped in the "on" position and the saw is controlled by a foot switch. It may be necessary to fasten the blade guard back out of the way.

Portable saw pinch-hits as a cutoff machine

■ A PORTABLE CIRCULAR SAW is the heart of this cutoff machine. Its abrasive blade slices through metal rods, pipes, angle iron and bars of various shapes with ease, even through hardened steel that a hacksaw won't touch.

The machine consists essentially of a metal framework that supports the saw vertically and nose-down, with a swinging unit to which the material to be cut is clamped. Swinging this "workholder" through a short arc by a handle projecting upward from it feeds the work against the edge of the abrasive blade. Shields help provide safety and protect the user from sparks and particles generated by the grinding action.

The abrasive disc normally used is an aluminum-oxide type designed for cutting steel and other metals. Dimensions given can be altered easily to accommodate a saw of a different make.

The saw-supporting frame is made by riveting together two ⅛ x 1¼ x 11¾-in. steel bars and two ¾ x ¾ x 11¼-in. pieces of angle iron. The frame is mounted on a plywood base with three bolts, and braced by two lengths of ½-in.-o.d. tubing flattened at the ends. The bars are positioned on

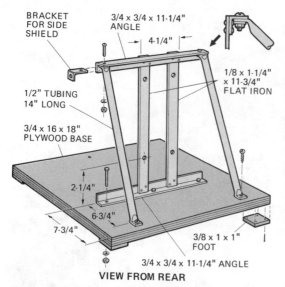

BRACKET
FOR SIDE
SHIELD

3/4 x 3/4 x 11-1/4"
ANGLE

4-1/4"

1/8 x 1-1/4"
x 11-3/4"
FLAT IRON

1/2" TUBING
14" LONG

3/4 x 16 x 18"
PLYWOOD BASE

2-1/4"

6-3/4"

7-3/4"

3/8 x 1 x 1"
FOOT

3/4 x 3/4 x 11-1/4" ANGLE

VIEW FROM REAR

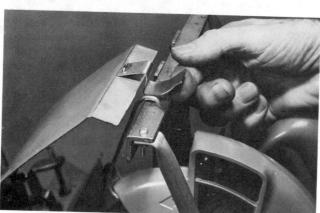

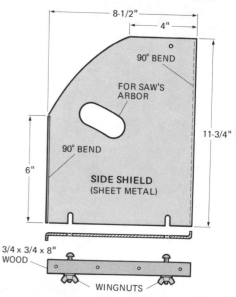

8-1/2"

4"

90° BEND

FOR SAW'S
ARBOR

11-3/4"

90° BEND

6"

SIDE SHIELD
(SHEET METAL)

3/4 x 3/4 x 8"
WOOD

WINGNUTS

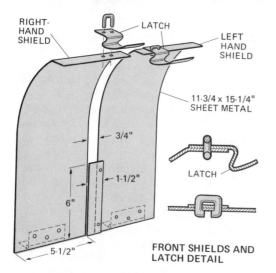

RIGHT-
HAND
SHIELD

LATCH

LEFT
HAND
SHIELD

11-3/4 x 15-1/4"
SHEET METAL

3/4"

LATCH

1-1/2"

6"

5-1/2"

**FRONT SHIELDS AND
LATCH DETAIL**

AN ELONGATED OPENING in the sheet-metal side
shield (photo, top) accommodates long workpieces. The
control handle has a plastic grip over the end.

THE FRAME which holds the saw vertically is bolted to
the baseboard and held rigid by two diagonal braces as
shown in the drawing at the upper left.

A SIMPLE LATCH holds each curved shield closed. The
latch is easily flipped open, but will lock automatically
when the shields are swung to their closed position.

the angle pieces so that two holes drilled in each to receive 10-24 bolts will align with similar holes already in the base plate of the circular saw.

The bottom angle strip is fastened to the plywood baseboard with 10-24 bolts. So the lower ends of the bolts would clear the bench top, five blocks about ⅜-in. thick were glued to the baseboard (one at each corner and one near the center) to serve as "feet." In mounting the frame, the two tubular braces are positioned so the bars remain perpendicular to the baseboard.

The saw is attached to the frame with short 10-24 bolts, lock washers and nuts. It is positioned so its lower tip clears the metal angle by approximately ⅛ in.

The swinging workholder is made by bolting together two thicknesses of ¾-in. plywood. Dimensions are not particularly critical so long as the assembly can be swung without binding against the baseboard, and the V-groove for holding workpieces is at approximately the same height above the baseboard as the center of the abrasive blade.

The workholder pivots on a ½ x 10-in. steel shaft extending between two identical pillow blocks. A V-shaped channel, in which a piece of angle iron measuring 1¼ x 1¼ x 6½ in. is secured, is formed by the two 45° plywood edges. Centered ¾ in. up from the bottom edge is a ½-in. hole for the shaft. This hole can be formed by roughing a near-semicircular groove in each plywood half on a circular saw and finishing it

with a gouge and rasp. The finished groove is a little less than ¼ in. deep.

Shaft ends rest in holes bored in the pillow blocks and should be a rather tight fit. If you adjust the two lower bolts that pass through the plywood halves, friction can be maintained and all play eliminated. The shaft grooves are coated lightly with grease. In mounting the pillow blocks, holes were made oversize so the blocks could be shifted to eliminate end play of the

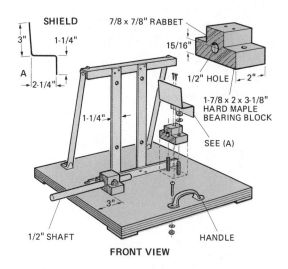

FRONT VIEW

HOLD-DOWN CLAMPS (below) are made from steel strips and attached with ¼-20 x 2-in. carriage bolts. Angle iron fits a channel formed by plywood pieces and is fastened with two flathead wood screws.

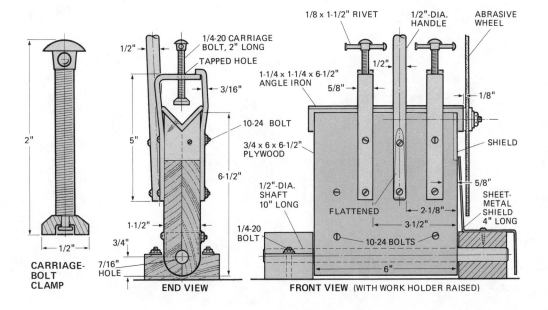

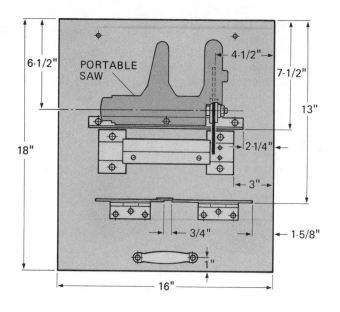

workholder and to align the angle-iron channel with the saw blade.

Two screw clamps, made and installed as shown, secure work in the channel of the swinging workholder. Both clamps are bent to an L-shape from $3/16$ x $5/8$-in. steel bar stock; and the clamp nearest the wheel is further stiffened by a "hook" made from similar material. This hook prevents the clamp screw from springing upward when tightened. Ideally, both clamps should completely encircle the V-channel as shown.

The clamp screws are made from $1/4$-20 x 2-in. carriage bolts. The bolt tips are fitted with loose collars like those on conventional C-clamps. The collars are lathe-turned and the bolt ends turned down to fit loosely in the collar holes, after which the ends are peened over with the aid of a punch. The cross handles, extending through holes drilled just below the bolt heads, are $1/8$ x $1\frac{1}{2}$-in. rivets.

The handle, which is attached near the middle of the workholder, is a 12-in. length of $1/2$-in. steel rod, somewhat flattened at the lower end where

PILLOW BLOCKS are mounted to position the shaft so that the work-holding assembly will clear the blade. The hinge is for one of the curved front shields.

THE SWINGING WORKHOLDER must position the workpiece perpendicular to the side of the abrasive blade if you are to be sure of obtaining a square cut.

two bolts are used to fasten it to the wood workholder. Add a length of plastic tubing to the end to provide a grip.

Installing the shields

Shields made from heavy-gauge sheet steel help to protect against possible breakage, and against flying sparks and particles produced by the grinding operation. The curved front shield is 5 in. wide and positioned to be approximately centered with the blade. Its lower end is attached to the baseboard with a butt hinge so the shield can be swung out of the way when mounting or removing work.

While the swinging workholder fills the space fairly well on the motor side of the blade, add a second curved shield in front of the machine and mount it alongside the first with a space of almost 1 in. in between for the workholder lever. The lower 6-in. portion of this gap is blocked by a sheet-metal strip riveted to the right-hand shield.

At the upper end of each shield is a self-locking latch which engages metal angle to hold it in closed position. The latches are so shaped so they cannot be disengaged by outward pressure against the shield. They must be lifted by a finger.

Another sheet-metal shield is bent to fit over the pillow block beneath the abrasive blade to fend off sparks and grit. It extends upward between blade and workholder and overlaps a small metal shield nailed to the end of the workholder. Two wood screws fasten the pillow-block shield in place.

The side shield is at right angles to the curved shield and covers much of the side of the machine to intercept flying sparks and particles. Two notches in its lower edge engage 6-32 bolts that clamp it against a wooden strip fastened to the baseboard. The upper corner of the side shield is attached to the saw-supporting frame with an L-shaped bracket and bolt. An elongated opening permits long workpieces to pass through.

The machine is turned on and off by a foot switch. The switch in the saw handle is taped in the "on" position and all starting and stopping is controlled by the foot.

The portable saw used has a pivoted guard that, if not restrained, covers too much of the blade in cutoff work. It is locked partly open with a C-shaped wire hooked through a hole in the top metal angle.

A cutoff machine of this type is essentially a grinder, and grinders can throw out a lot of gritty dirt and voluminous sparks. So such a tool should not be used where it might cause trouble with other equipment or with personnel, or near easily ignitable material. No one should stand where, in the event of wheel breakage, flying pieces might cause injury. Children, especially, should be kept away. The machine should be checked frequently to determine whether all shields are in position and secured, and that other parts are functioning properly. The operator should wear approved safety goggles or a face mask, and a breathing mask (respirator) is recommended.

Choosing an abrasive wheel

Manufacturers of portable circular saws often include abrasive blades among the accessories. Abrasive blades that are thicker than the regular saw blades may require a thinner inside washer to hold them properly in place. It is important that the saw speed in revolutions per minute should not exceed the recommended maximum rpm specified by the manufacturer of the abrasive wheel you are using. If the speed of the saw you are using is too high, consider purchasing a motor speed control that the saw can be plugged into. These are widely available at hardware stores and contain the proper circuitry to allow you to adjust the saw speed continuously from 0 rpm to the saw's maximum speed.

During cutting, especially of sizable stock, it is a good idea to stop and examine the clamps frequently to make certain the workpiece remains firmly held.

Using power planes

■ IF YOU'RE thinking about buying a power plane, rent one for a weekend the next time you plan to do a lot of planing. Heft the tool about and use it on practice cuts. Once you've mastered the art of getting the spinning cutter on and off the edge to be cut without making a dip—thus a gouge—you'll want your own.

Basically, a power plane does everything a hand plane does. The difference is that the planing job becomes effortless because the tool does all the work. You simply guide it.

The power plane, depending upon its maker, will have a spinning blade with one or more cutting edges, located not quite halfway back from the leading edge of the tool. To obtain depth-of-cut, the front shoe adjusts up or down (in the same fashion that a stationary shop jointer does).

Because the entire cutter on the bottom is exposed when the tool is in use, it should be used with extreme caution. Virtually every manufacturer includes a thorough manual with its tool. Read it through—especially the section dealing with safety. No matter which brand you buy, you'll find that handles and gripping portions of the tool are well away from the blade while the tool is in use. *Make certain you grip the tool as the manufacturer specifies.*

While it's no secret that power planes can make short work out of many planing tasks, they can also cause a great deal of trouble if they are not used properly. The two most common mis-takes are improper tool alignment when starting and when finishing cuts. The best way to avoid these mistakes is to spend time practicing on a variety of scrap wood before you put the tool to any finish work.

Tool alignment is particularly crucial when planing the end grain of stock because the edge is normally quite short. To do this properly, hold the tool as shown in the photos and make a short pass in one direction—about 1 in. into the stock—then finish the cut from the other direction. The two cuts should meet flush, keeping you from splitting off any stock when you come to the long edge of the board.

Don't assume power planes are designed only for edge planing. These tools can be used for surface planing as well. Just keep in mind that scant stock removal is the best policy. If you have the cutter set too deep, these powerful tools can make

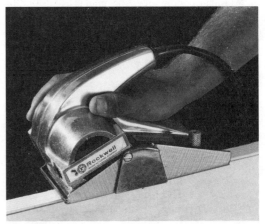

A WELL-MAINTAINED POWER PLANE with its super-sharp cutter allows for fast removal of large amounts of edge stock. The tool can also be used to remove surface stock.

HERE ARE LEFT AND RIGHT SIDE VIEWS of a power planer. This rugged model is particularly outstanding when you have extensive planing sessions.

severe gouges in a surface, almost before you know it's happening. It's a better idea to make several shallow cuts until the surface is flat.

Another great use for the power plane is to cut rabbets along a board edge. To do this, you must have a planer equipped with a fence that func-tions in much the same way that a rip guide oper-ates on a circular saw. By adjusting this fence in and out, you can regulate how far across the board the cutter will extend and, therefore, the width of the rabbet. The depth adjustment on the tool itself regulates the depth of the rabbet.

THE DEPTH-OF-CUT KNOB is rotated in order to achieve the particular cut you want.

THE ARROW ON THE KNOB serves as the pointer for aligning with index.

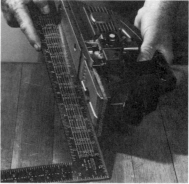

BEFORE STARTING A CUT, the shoe should be checked with a straight-edge.

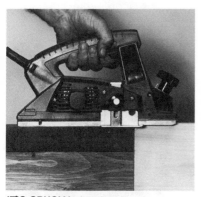

IT'S CRUCIAL that the plane be posi-tioned properly before starting. It should rest flat on the board edge, as shown here, with the cutter not yet touching the wood.

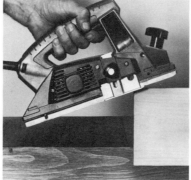

THIS EXAGGERATED POSE shows the wrong way to start a planing pass. But even if the back of the tool is just slightly lower, you will get a dip at the beginning of the cut.

TOP BOARD SHOWS scoop that re-sults from dropping rear of plane at beginning of cut. Bottom piece shows edge planed properly.

MAINTAINING THE SAME FLAT TOOL ALIGNMENT is equally impor-tant at the other end of a planing pass. Be sure the tool remains level until the cutter has moved completely clear of the board's edge.

THIS PHOTO SHOWS an exaggerated dip at the end of a cut. Be sure to watch for this tendency until you mas-ter the tool.

IF YOU DO LET the front of the blade dip as it leaves the edge of the stock, you will get a gouge like the one above.

Power tool tips

LACKING DRUM SANDERS of the correct size for some inside curves, we found that sections of dowel could be used to serve the purpose. A slot was cut in the end of the dowel and a strip of sandpaper inserted and wrapped around the dowel. We have used these sanders in the drill press and on portable electric drills. When the ends of the paper become worn, pieces are torn off and the ''sanders'' are like new again.

TO RAISE THE SPEED of my 9-in. metalworking lathe from 1270 rpm (slow for small-diameter work, polishing and wood turning) to 3800 rpm, add an extra 5-in. V-pulley to motor and jackshaft pulleys. The pulley hubs were machined to fit over the projecting stub shafts, bolted to the face of existing pulleys and fitted with a V-belt cut to fit.

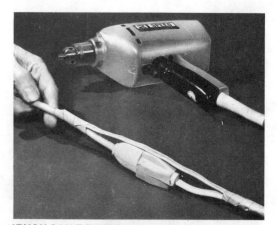

IF YOU CAN'T FIND a regular ''cord connector'' for reinforcing extension-cord connections, you can make one from a length of lamp cord or small rope and masking tape. When no longer needed, the reinforcement is quickly removed by peeling off the tape.

WHEN USING A DISC SANDER on a painted floor, the paper can become so paint clogged before it was worn it was no longer effective. By using paint remover and cleaning off softened paint you get more mileage.

BY CLAMPING A ROUTER upside down, you can use it as a stationary tool to burnish scroll workpieces. Insert a short length of ¼-in. steel rod in the collet, tighten and feed the work against the spinning rod.

WHEN END-DRILLING some hardwood dowels in a lathe, the small drill bit tends to wander off center. After inserting the bit deeply into the chuck, you will be able to drill the axial holes accurately.

WHEN USING a fast-cutting power sander to smooth a small, flat surface such as the lid of a trinket box, you can avoid accidental overcutting at the edges by surrounding the work with wood. The protective wood border can be made by clamping strips flush with the top surface.

AN ADJUSTABLE PIVOT sliding in a slotted length of angle iron that's attached to the table of your jigsaw makes a handy fixture for cutting true discs. The detail shows how the pivot and its Tee-nut point rests in a blind hole drilled in a machine screw. This permits removing the pivot and driving it into the underside of the work. How the fixture is attached to the machine depends on the table itself. If it has a lip, like the one shown, it can be attached with C-clamps.

SAWDUST ACCUMULATION along the fence of your radial-arm saw can be avoided with this self-clearing device. Simply bore a row of ¾-in. holes along the edge of the front table insert. Thus when you slide the work along the fence to position it, the board automatically pushes the sawdust down through the holes to the floor. If you prefer, you can achieve the same results by making the holes in the edge of an auxiliary table and using it as shown in the photo.

A MITERBOX will support your work while you cut small pieces of wood or metal with a sabre saw. This keeps the free end of a workpiece from vibrating when you're working on the other end, a problem which arises if the work is supported in a vise. Simply set the work over the miterbox, letting the saw blade cut between the two uprights. If you don't have a suitably deep miterbox, try improvising a simple sawing jig from a length of 2 x 4 and a few pieces of scrap pine.

SHOP GUIDE

CUSTOMARY TO METRIC (CONVERSION)
Conversion factors can be carried so far they become impractical. In cases below where an entry is exact it is followed by an asterisk (*). Where considerable rounding off has taken place, the entry is followed by a + or a − sign.

Linear Measure

inches	millimeters
1/16	1.5875*
1/8	3.2
3/16	4.8
1/4	6.35*
5/16	7.9
3/8	9.5
7/16	11.1
1/2	12.7*
9/16	14.3
5/8	15.9
11/16	17.5
3/4	19.05*
13/16	20.6
7/8	22.2
15/16	23.8
1	25.4*

inches	centimeters
1	2.54*
2	5.1
3	7.6
4	10.2
5	12.7*
6	15.2
7	17.8
8	20.3
9	22.9
10	25.4*
11	27.9
12	30.5

feet	centimeters	meters
1	30.48*	.3048*
2	61	.61
3	91	.91
4	122	1.22
5	152	1.52
6	183	1.83
7	213	2.13
8	244	2.44
9	274	2.74
10	305	3.05
50	1524*	15.24*
100	3048*	30.48*

1 yard = .9144* meters
1 rod = 5.0292* meters
1 mile = 1.6 kilometers
1 nautical mile = 1.852* kilometers

Weights

ounces	grams
1	28.3
2	56.7
3	85
4	113
5	142
6	170
7	198
8	227
9	255
10	283
11	312
12	340
13	369
14	397
15	425
16	454

Formula (exact):
ounces × 28.349 523 125* = grams

pounds	kilograms
1	.45
2	.9
3	1.4
4	1.8
5	2.3
6	2.7
7	3.2
8	3.6
9	4.1
10	4.5

1 short ton (2000 lbs) = 907 kilograms (kg)
Formula (exact):
pounds × .453 592 37* = kilograms

Fluid Measure

(Milliliters [ml] and cubic centimeters [cc] are equivalent, but it is customary to use milliliters for liquids.)

1 cu in = 16.39 ml
1 fl oz = 29.6 ml
1 cup = 237 ml
1 pint = 473 ml
1 quart = 946 ml
    = .946 liters
1 gallon = 3785 ml
    = 3.785 liters
Formula (exact):
fluid ounces × 29.573 529 562 5* = milliliters

Volume

1 cu in = 16.39 cubic centimeters (cc)
1 cu ft = 28 316.7 cc
1 bushel = 35 239.1 cc
1 peck = 8 809.8 cc

Area

1 sq in = 6.45 sq cm
1 sq ft = 929 sq cm
    = .093 sq meters
1 sq yd = .84 sq meters
1 acre = 4 046.9 sq meters
    = .404 7 hectares
1 sq mile = 2 589 988 sq meters
    = 259 hectares
    = 2.589 9 sq kilometers

Miscellaneous

1 British thermal unit (Btu) (mean)
    = 1 055.9 joules
1 horsepower = 745.7 watts
        = .75 kilowatts
caliber (diameter of a firearm's bore in hundredths of an inch)
    = .254 millimeters (mm)

1 atmosphere pressure = 101 325* pascals (newtons per sq meter)
1 pound per square inch (psi) = 6 895 pascals
1 pound per square foot = 47.9 pascals
1 knot = 1.85 kilometers per hour
1 mile per hour = 1.6093 kilometers per hour